PENGUIN BOOKS

THE OTHER SIDE
OF THE FIRE

Alice Thomas Ellis was born in Liverpool before the war and was educated at Bangor Grammar School and Liverpool School of Art. She has written five novels: *The Sin Eater* (1977), which received a Welsh Arts Council Award for 'a book of exceptional merit'; *The Birds of the Air* (1980, Penguin 1983), which also won a Welsh Arts Council Award; *The 27th Kingdom* (Penguin, 1982), which was nominated for the Booker Prize, *The Other Side of the Fire*, and *Unexplained Laughter*.

Under her real name (Anna Haycraft) she has written two cookery books, *Natural Baby Food* and, with Caroline Blackwood, *Darling, You Shouldn't Have Gone to So Much Trouble* (1980).

She is married to Colin Haycraft, chairman and managing director of Duckworth, publishers, of which she is a director and the fiction editor. They have five children.

Alice Thomas Ellis

THE OTHER SIDE
OF THE FIRE

Penguin Books

For Tom Pitt Aikens

Penguin Books Ltd, Harmondsworth, Middlesex, England
Viking Penguin Inc., 40 West 23rd Street, New York, New York, 10010, U.S.A.
Penguin Books Australia Ltd, Ringwood, Victoria, Australia
Penguin Books Canada Limited, 2801 John Street, Markham, Ontario, Canada L3R 1B4
Penguin Books (N.Z.) Ltd, 182-190 Wairau Road, Auckland 10, New Zealand

First published by Gerald Duckworth & Co. Ltd 1983
Published in Penguin Books 1985
Reprinted 1986

Made and printed in Great Britain by
Richard Clay (The Chaucer Press) Ltd,
Bungay, Suffolk
Typeset in Century Schoolbook

Such is the will of Venus
('Tis but a cruel joke)
To link unlikely people
Beneath a brazen yoke.

Horace

1

On the last day of summer Mrs Bohannon fell in love. The poplars, fallaciously pathetic, looked horrified, their branches rising on the wind like startled hair, and a pilgrim cloud wept a few chill tears.

It began in a garden, as these things will, and she fell in love with her husband's son.

Bloody hell!

It happened like this ...

*

It was a Sunday afternoon and Charles Bohannon was sleeping the sleep of one who has just eaten Sunday lunch. He lay at a diagonal slant in a wing chair with one ear bent against a harsh plush cheek. Also, his mouth was slightly open and therefore dry. He woke, naturally, in a bad mood.

'Tea not ready yet?' he said.

Claudia Bohannon rose, put down the newspaper which she had been unsuccessfully scrutinising for something which would hold her interest to the end and, instead of going to the kitchen, went through the hall to the garden door. She took a long white scarf from a peg, wound it thrice about her neck and went outside.

She had not, until recently, thought of herself as a discontented or a rebellious woman. She had watched from the battlemented safety of an incurious mind the antics of other women as they removed their bras and strove to expel gender distinctions from the language. She had not understood their purpose. For fifteen years she had accepted, had taken pleasure in, the role of the English Housewife, enjoying the sense of continuity that it gave her. She had liked her house with its polished wood, its old rugs, its bowls of flowers. In the novels that she read country houses smelled like her own house, of wax polish and roses or chrysanthemums according to the season, and this had given her a sense of personal reality. She had particularly liked her kitchen and the pantry with its rows of shelves holding jars of jam and bottled fruit. Sometimes she had wished she cured her own hams, but this would, logically, have entailed the keeping and killing of her own pigs; and that, she felt, would have been affectation. But often she had made her own bread. She had had an image of herself as central to a microcosm of English society. Now that image was losing definition – worse, it seemed to be losing its appeal, and Claudia sometimes had the disconcerting feeling that she was losing herself.

Since her children had gone away to school she had wished that she could do her own housework, but that would have meant getting rid of Edith who came in three times a week and relied on her wages for the money to go on holiday to Malta or Ostend with her mother and her husband and the twins. Claudia was glad that Charles was so untidy, because if it hadn't been for his wandering socks, overflowing ashtrays and muddled papers she would have had almost nothing to do. She was bored, and irritated by her own predictability. While she had never thought of herself as an exceptional person, neither had she imagined, as life went by, that she would respond to its vicissitudes with such totally conventional reactions. Now, like someone approaching the end of adolescence, she found herself chafing at the confines of home. Like a liveried servant she began to wish that she could return to her husband all that he had lent her to keep out the cold. She had given her life into his keeping and he had put it away like a garment, neatly cleaned and ironed and never to be worn. In return he had bestowed on her the respectable habiliments of the wife and mother – the apron, the milk-soaked blouse, the blood-stained knickers, the coat made of the skins of animals that was her reward for conjugality, and cold, shining little jewels that she never wore since she had seen other women wearing theirs and had despised them. Those women, in their rings and necklaces, had had a stamped, a franked appearance that did credit neither to them nor to their owners. It had been, to date, her only rebellion and had arisen from taste rather than insight. Stirring within her Claudia now felt the desire to wear what she had never worn – the strange and garish garment of her self. She found she wanted to go about the world in freedom, unrecognisable and subject to no one.

All this was partly due to her friend, Sylvie, but Claudia was not aware of it. Women, said Sylvie, are basically so alike, their interests so similar, that they affect each other imperceptibly like the members of a primitive tribe or a band of hunted outcasts. Among women individuality is of little account. Sylvie had told her often that what women want is to be recognised, accepted and appreciated as separate and distinct from men. If, Sylvie had said, Sigmund Freud hadn't already made up his mind that if what women wanted wasn't clear to him it couldn't be clear to anybody, he might have thrown up his window, leaned out and asked almost any passer-by. And after a little thought that's what they'd have told him. All confusion, Sylvie maintained, arose from one inability – that of men to see anything beyond their own noses (she hadn't said noses), their belief that women are incomplete men and therefore racked with rage and jealousy.

Claudia hadn't taken much notice of her, and Charles had held that Sylvie wasn't all there.

Brooding wordlessly, Claudia drifted across the garden.

Philip, her husband's son, was far away tying up some Michaelmas daisies against the depredations of the wind.

She walked through the cold until she came to him. He was kneeling. His cheekbones were as high and curved and gleaming as the crescent moon. She stood looking down at him, and after a moment she began to cry.

Then he got up and with an earth-laden finger he wiped her tears away; first one side then the other.

'Your face is dirty,' he said.

And Mrs Bohannon was lost.

*

Philip was gentle. What is more he had spoken of her face as though it belonged to her; unlike his father, who, Claudia felt sure, thought of her face as *his* face, one of his many rightful possessions. Being seen as a separate second person made Claudia feel extraordinary. Even her parents, she believed, had thought of her face as *their* face, and she knew her children did. For a moment she was that curious thing, a female in her own possession. It was a moment's manumission before she was forced to remember that the tyranny of obsessive love leaves other tyrannies well behind.

At first she had no idea what had happened to her. She merely congratulated herself on the sweetness of her relations with her stepson as they shopped and gardened and cooked together. She realised after a while that her last thoughts before sleeping were of Philip, and her first waking thoughts, and, what is more, most of her thoughts in between, but she did not see or accept the significance of this. Then one day she scalded her fingers while draining the potatoes for supper and cried out, and Philip leapt across the kitchen and took her hand in his, making noises of commiseration and pity and Claudia quite forgot the pain in an overwhelming sensation of lust.

She said aloud, 'Bloody hell,' which was very unlike her.

2

'When can Philip start work?' Claudia asked her husband the following morning. Until now Philip had lived with his mother and her lovers, working in her Literary Agency. The latest lover had not cared for this arrangement and Philip himself had grown bored with it. It seemed only sensible that he should return to Oxford, join his father's printing works and eventually succeed to the ownership. Claudia, despite some maternal misgivings on behalf of her own children, had seen the justice in this. Philip was, after all, the eldest son.

'When Harris goes,' said Charles. 'It's been difficult enough finding Philip a place without sacking someone. Harris is only going because I wouldn't give him a rise. I don't feel good about it. It's been very awkward.'

Claudia felt sorry for the disgruntled Harris, but not very. 'I think nepotism is a good idea,' she said contrarily. 'Like bribery. They make everything much easier and cut through all that red tape.' Her husband's narrow view of morality increasingly annoyed her.

'Don't be stupid,' said Charles.

But Claudia, like most women, was an honourable person. Sylvie held that whereas men thrive on competition, deceit and destruction, women who bear the burden of continuing the race find it necessary on the whole to behave in a limpid and straightforward way. They are too much concerned with life to have much time for plotting and scheming and reducing civilisations to rubble –

although there are, of course, unhappy exceptions. What was wrong, Claudia asked herself defiantly, with a little nepotism or gentle bribery? They were surely preferable to the ruthless competition which would inevitably make many people feel inadequate and unhappy.

When she stopped feeling angry, she found, once more rising about her, that sensation of moving, half-blinded, through honeyed cobwebs that commonly goes with the early stages of love. So, being an honourable person, she attempted to lie to herself. She told herself in so many words that her fondness for Philip's company was the result of her missing her own children, that the weakness she felt in his presence was caused by a viral infection, that what she saw in Philip was some reflection of his father. She didn't believe herself. Philip was, for one thing, nothing like his father. He was like his mother.

Then I've gone mad, concluded Claudia. What could be madder than falling in love with someone who resembled the person you'd once hated most in all the world? What uncharted depths of human weirdness had she chanced upon? She remembered with some mirth that, when Philip was a little boy, for a time she'd hated him too.

'Well, I'm blessed,' she said aloud. There was a wasp in the silent kitchen. It stumbled along the window ledge, swearing. 'Always a wasp,' she said, wondering why she'd taken to talking to herself. She opened the window to let it out, but it wouldn't go, so she beat it to death with the dishcloth.

*

Claudia telephoned Sylvie. She said very bravely: 'Sylvie, is Evvie going to be home this weekend?'

'She's home,' said Sylvie. 'She's brought her washing, she's devastated the attic looking for old magazines and she's writing a book. I may kill her.'

'Well, send her round for supper first,' said Claudia. 'I

want someone young for Philip. He's getting bored with just us.'

'He won't get much change out of Evvie. She's a man-hater,' said Evvie's mother. 'She'll never get married and she's probably going to insist on living with me for ever in dutiful-daughter fashion. She won't stay in her college during term time like everyone else doing whatever they do. She says she's going to try and come home every weekend. I may kill myself.'

At first sight it was hard to see why Evvie should rouse these feelings in her mother. She was a small self-confident girl with a pointed face and straight brown hair. It was only when they had been with her for some time that people began to wonder if self-confidence might not have its negative aspects. Evvie's self-confidence seemed to exclude all other human beings and most emotions. Claudia thought it might be due to her youth, but Evvie didn't seem very young. Rather she seemed ageless. Her clothes looked as though they'd been hastily and thoughtlessly assembled out of a Bring-and-Buy that had happened some years ago, and this made her seem timeless. Today she had chosen to appear in a torn muslin skirt and a stained and balding blue velvet jacket. Claudia couldn't help wondering why. Still, perhaps she was irresistible to people of her own age.

'Evvie,' said Claudia, 'do you remember Philip? You met years ago when you were little.'

'Hi,' said Evvie.

'Do you remember Evvie, Philip?' asked Claudia. 'She's my goddaughter.'

'Hi,' said Philip.

Well, I tried, Claudia told herself as she went to the kitchen to slice the cold tongue. I brought the young people together. Not my fault if it doesn't work.

'Where's Charles?' asked Evvie as they sat at the kitchen table. Her tone was faintly aggrieved.

'He's still at the office,' said Claudia. 'Printing's going

13

through a very difficult time. He has to work most evenings.' Her own tone was slightly reproving.

'He said he'd lend me a pamphlet about how to set out a manuscript,' said Evvie, now sounding sulky. 'I want to get my novel absolutely right before it goes off for setting.'

'Have you got a publisher?' asked Philip. He hadn't spoken for some time but clearly could not resist this.

'It isn't finished yet,' said Evvie. She seemed to think there was no more to be said on the matter and ate a lot of tongue and salad in unselfconscious silence.

'What's it about?' asked Philip.

It was now obvious to Claudia that he had taken a dislike to Evvie and was bent on teasing her in the way that men tease women who they consider lack a proper appreciation of their place in the order of things. 'Yes, do tell us,' she said quickly. 'Wait a moment while I get the pudding.'

'It's about two brothers called Fungus and Mango,' Philip told her as she returned with the blackberry pie.

'Fergus and Mungo, you fool,' said Evvie dispassionately. 'It's a soppy love story.'

'What about your degree?' enquired Claudia, sounding to herself depressingly elderly and sensible.

'I'll get that,' said Evvie dislodging a blackberry pip with the nail of her little finger, 'but there's no money in academic life.' Evvie was reading Greats, as classics and philosophy were called in Oxford. It was what all the clever people read who weren't scientists, and it was completely useless.

'Do go on about your novel,' said Claudia having just observed Philip's latest expression.

'Well, there was this amazing coincidence,' said Evvie, putting down her fork. 'I've read something like a million women's magazines to get the form right, and I sort of knew the characters I wanted, but I hadn't got them quite worked out. You've got to have them first, and you have to know them well or you won't know what they're going to do. Character being plot, you understand.' She looked at

14

them both in turn to make sure they did. 'Then a couple of weeks ago Gloria was acting up and Mum made me take her to the vet – he lives in that skinny house beyond Bagley Woods with the field in front and the jersey cow in it – and the vet turned out to be Scotch, so that was it.'

'Oh yes?' said Philip with the barbed courtesy of simulated incomprehension.

'*The Scotch vet*,' said Evvie, beating the table with a knife handle for emphasis. 'He's one of the heroes of World Literature. Theseus, Odysseus, Mark Antony, Don Juan, Heathcliff, Rhett Butler, the Scotch vet – well, maybe not world literature, but he's a pillar of women's fiction. And there he was, large as life. And not just him. He's got a housekeeper and a brother and a fiancée and they all conform peculiarly to type. So all I have to do is observe them closely, imagine them in some suitable location and write it all down.'

'Sounds easy,' said Philip, looking as if he thought it sounded contemptible.

'Men won't like it,' said Evvie, 'but they don't have to. It's women who buy books.'

As Philip was evidently about to remark that women bought tripe, Claudia spoke again.

'I want to know what happens,' she said. And she did. She thought for the moment that she would prefer this story to her own. 'I can't imagine how you found out all about his family on one visit.'

'Oh, I've been back,' said Evvie casually. 'Three or four times. I found some dead old bird and I pretended I thought it was just ill, and I took it to him. And when he said it'd snuffed it I cried, so they asked me to tea.

'You are awful, Evvie,' said Claudia, 'but go on.'

'Well,' continued Evvie, 'Fungus ... *damn*. That's your fault,' she accused Philip. 'They'll always be Fungus and Mango now. Anyway, Fungus – he's the vet – has this fiancée. She's a little brown number in jeans scuttling round with trays of fairy cakes and pots of steaming tea in

15

a tea-cosy, and she's got piles of shiny brown curls like fresh dog shit and she's a bit shy, only under all that she's really not just clinging but quite possessive too.'

'She sounds a bit boring,' ventured Claudia.

'She *is* boring,' said Evvie gloomily. 'She's as boring as all hell. But then she's got to be. The Scotch vet's fiancée has to be boring to offset the wicked and lovely outsider who comes along to gum up the works.'

'You could change her in some way,' suggested Claudia, who had never essayed the art of novel writing.

'No, I couldn't,' said Evvie. 'My muse would be offended if I tried to change her. You have to take what the fates send along or they get nasty and take your inspiration away from you. You have to have faith. It'll all work out for the best in the end. Anyway I'm stuck with the blooming girl. She's a teacher with a degree in Eng.Lit. from some polytechnic and when you telephone and the vet's busy unpicking some budgerigar she says he isn't *available* ... Oh God. She's called Clara,' added Evvie with an exasperated frown. 'The Scotch vet's a bore too – a true Caledonian boar.' She giggled.

'You're a snob, Evvie,' said Claudia, but gently.

'I know,' said Evvie. 'All my generation is. The left's out of style – punts and cocktails are back. It heralds a revival of fascism.'

'And who's Mango?' enquired Claudia, out of her depth.

Evvie looked more cheerful. 'He's the scapegrace younger brother,' she said, 'a trial to them all with his racing cars and his women. Won't hold down a job. I really believe in him.'

'And the wicked and lovely outsider?'

Evvie sat up and pushed her chair back, looking truly animated. 'Amaryllis,' she said. 'Amaryllis is all mine. I'm making her up out of whole cloth Hair as black as the raven's wing, eyes with the cold fire of emeralds, and a sick wolfhound. I think she probably loves that wolfhound more

than anything else in the whole world. He's how she gets to
meet the vet. The vet – I mean, really the vet – has got a
pet cow and two cats called ...' She paused. 'I have to be
very careful how I say this,' she explained. Evvie was one of
those who, when speaking of rodents, says mats and rice;
once when Claudia had given her *coq au vin* for supper she
had told her mother that Claudia had kicked a chooken.
Eyes crossed slightly in concentration as she completed her
sentence, she told them that the animals were known as
Catface and Runt. 'I just call them "you",' she said. 'I
think they're probably Bridie's familiars. I may make her a
witch.'

'It sounds a terrible book,' said Claudia frankly.

'It *is* terrible,' agreed Evvie. 'It'll make my fortune.'

'But I don't see why, if you want to write, you don't write
a proper book,' said Claudia rather confusedly.

Evvie, however, understood her meaning. 'I know my
limitations,' she said unexpectedly, 'and I seem to have a
gift for writing rubbish. It's very lucky.'

'My mother's got a wolfhound,' said Philip. 'She uses a
picture of one on the firm's writing paper.'

'I remember it,' said Claudia, determined to be sensible.
It was years since she'd needed to worry about Philip's
mother. She could visualise the tiny silhouette as clearly as
if it lay before her. A dog with the precise perfection of a
punctuation mark.

'What's your mother's firm for?' asked Evvie.

'It's a Literary Agency,' said Philip, looking at her
sideways under his lashes. 'What do you think of that
then?'

'I think it's very fortunate,' said Evvie promptly. 'Why
didn't anybody tell me? She can handle my book.'

Claudia crumbled a crust of bread. She didn't, even
now, want Philip's mother back in their lives, not even on
the periphery.

'You've worried me,' said Philip, 'with a vision of the

Scotch vet running his hands through all that dog shit.'

'I won't put it like that in the book,' promised Evvie. 'I'll say she had gleaming ringlets.'

*

Sylvie was making the most of her daughter's absence. She poured herself half a tumbler of gin and added some token tonic. Evvie disapproved of her mother drinking and coughed exaggeratedly whenever she smoked. Sylvie lit a cigarette.

She patted her lap as a sign to Gloria, who clambered laboriously up and lay across her knees, smiling. 'Why can't you always be good?' said Sylvie. Gloria had a jealous nature and often behaved as Sylvie's husband used to behave, being offensive to her friends (especially men) and causing scenes in public places.

Sylvie stared at the television set. Evvie didn't like her doing that either. She said her mother looked old and defeated when she sat there watching television. It was hard, thought Sylvie. Her girlhood had been largely spent in trying to hide from her mother what she was doing, and now it looked as though, in middle age, she would be similarly occupied in attempting to deceive her daughter.

She had left her husband long ago and spent years in comparative freedom. Evvie, it seemed, was no longer prepared to let her get away with it. Sylvie wondered what had happened to the permissive and loose-living young. All the ones she'd met recently were dauntingly moralistic. They ate Health Foods, and while, admittedly, they didn't get married much they paired off very early and stayed together for ages and ages. They made her feel immature, an axolotl. Evvie even worried that her mother had no sex life. 'It's bad for you,' she had told her. 'You're still a young woman. It's unnatural to live like a virgin hermit. You should fall in love.'

But Sylvie was cured of love and could no longer remember what all the fuss was about. She was like a child who, on having the facts of life explained to her, wishes only that now someone would explain why people should choose to engage in such bizarre behaviour. 'Anyway,' she'd said, 'I haven't noticed that *you're* tied up in a passionate and rewarding relationship.'

'I have my work,' Evvie had responded. 'My novel and my thesis on Latin Love Elegy. I've got frightfully keen on Horace lately, and I don't fancy anyone else at the moment.'

'Well, nor do I,' Sylvie had retorted, 'so cut it out.'

She wondered whether other mothers and daughters had similar exchanges but thought it unlikely. To the best of her recollection most people put in a lot of time dissuading their nearest and dearest from sexual relationships, not encouraging them.

*

Claudia woke in the small hours: the time when the living see no hope, no light, no purpose; the time when the dying die. It was as black as hell. Her husband whom she loved was asleep beside her and she wished he was his son.

3

In the morning Claudia telephoned Sylvie again.

'Sylvie,' she said. 'I've done something insane.'

Sylvie assumed she'd bought a new lawn-mower without asking Charles, or booked an expensive holiday. Claudia did that sort of thing sometimes. It was her way of asserting her independence.

Claudia said: 'Listen, Sylvie. I've fallen in love.'

Sylvie, although she knew such things happened, could not take this seriously. It was like hearing of a natural disaster in Outer Mongolia. She felt regretful but not deeply concerned.

'Be careful,' she said. 'It can be dangerous at your age.' Even as she spoke she was aware that she had struck a discordant note. 'I'm sorry,' she added. 'You took me by surprise. I'm not thinking.'

'*Sylvie*,' said Claudia reprimandingly. She often said this in their exchanges, as though speaking to a charming but recalcitrant animal who could not be expected totally to understand but nevertheless must be rebuked for its failure to conform to human *mores*.

'Who with?' asked Sylvie, dimly remembering the form on these occasions. She didn't care who with, but knew she was expected to ask.

'You don't know him,' answered Claudia predictably. This, Sylvie remembered, was also part of the form. It meant that Claudia was not sure whether or not her passion was reciprocated.

But Claudia went on. She said, 'I think he loves me', and Sylvie, hearing this, thought she was probably right. It usually happened that way – a man would be attracted to a woman and she would respond. It was rarely that a woman conceived a passion for a man who showed no interest in her at all, like Phaedra and her wretched love. Just as well, really. Otherwise men would be fancying unresponsive women, and women would be yearning after indifferent men all over the place, and no one would ever get together with anyone else: a terrible chain of unrequited desire. Sylvie had an image of a tapestry portraying men and women tracking each other through woods, each bent on the one in front, and no one ever turning round. It made her laugh.

'Can I come and see you?' asked Claudia piteously.

'That'll be lovely,' lied Sylvie. 'We'll have a drink.'

*

Claudia drove carefully since her instinct was to drive fast and dangerously. She reminded herself that she was a mother, and mothers had to handle themselves tenderly as though they were old soup tureens.

The lanes were full of ponderous farm machinery lumbering from farmyard to field and back again, and at one point, where the Council was widening the road, a vast earth-mover browsed purposefully over a mound of clay.

To Claudia, in her bewilderment, it seemed that the country was inhabited by ancient monsters, like her mind, and the minotaur roamed the labyrinthine lanes, part horror, part flesh of her flesh. She had been brusque with Philip that morning. She had lost the feeling that they shared a delightful secret. Now she felt that the secret was all her own and she was consumed with fear that he, more than anyone else, should discover it.

*

Sylvie lived in what had been a gamekeeper's cottage. It lay among fields and was approached by a narrow muddy path. The incautious visitor usually fell over on this path since for a large part of the year it was negotiable only by wary and judicious slithering. On one side lay a wood, at once dense and straggly. To Claudia, as she slid slowly forwards, it looked like knitting worked by a school of lunatics who had flung it away in a frenzy.

Sylvie was in the garden, her hands full of weeds. She stood under a greengage tree staring across the fields.

'Why on earth don't you do something about that path?' called Claudia discontentedly. Her boots were clogged with mud and she was cold.

Sylvie turned slowly. 'I didn't hear the car,' she said.

'I left it by the lodge,' said Claudia. 'I didn't like the look of the drive.'

'It's all right,' said Sylvie coming towards her. 'Evvie goes up and down it on her motor bicycle.'

Claudia was wondering how Sylvie could bear to live in this depressed wilderness of tangled briar and sodden grass. She tried to remember what it was like in spring and the height of summer. She knew it was different.

'I'm sorry to disturb you,' she said formally, and then thought that that was absurd. Sylvie hadn't been doing anything except pretending to weed the garden. None the less Claudia knew she was intruding.

'It's all right,' said Sylvie again. 'I'll just make sure Gloria's locked in the outhouse. Then I'll get you some coffee.'

The cottage was cold too, the fire laid but unlit.

'Hang on,' said Sylvie. 'I'll just put a match to it. Evvie's taken a cat to the vet. She found it in the outhouse, full of pellets. The gamekeeper shoots cats. He says they get the pheasants. I prefer cats to pheasants.' She gazed at the fire for a while as though considering this.

Claudia, watching the rising smoke, was thinking that in a previous age Sylvie and her daughter would have been burnt for witches. She didn't particularly know why she thought so except that there had always been, throughout the ages, something suspect and threatening about women living alone. 'What am I going to do, Sylvie?' she asked and remembered that, when they weren't burning them, people had often asked these solitary women for advice.

'I don't suppose you're going to do anything,' said Sylvie unhelpfully. She clearly wasn't about to offer to toss together a little love potion.

'That's no good,' said Claudia, throwing up her hands in a grasping gesture. 'I'll have to do something.'

'Then you must make up your own mind,' said Sylvie, sitting cross-legged in front of the smoke.

'You're so damn moral, Sylvie,' said Claudia unfairly.

'No, I'm not,' said Sylvie. 'I don't think sex has much to do with morals. It's more a compulsion – like murder. Not at all in the same category as telling lies or robbing banks.'

Claudia had always found it difficult to follow Sylvie's thought processes. 'They're completely different,' she said.

But Sylvie had begun to think. Every now and then she said 'Yes' or 'No', and she went 'Mm' quite a lot. But she wasn't listening. She was thinking about love and death. She thought that love was a blowsy old boot and yet the closest relation of God's most respectable emissary, death. A half-sister, perhaps; employed in the kitchens below stairs while death, God's butler, saw to the order of things upstairs. She got everyone tipsy down there in the kitchen and made terrible trouble for her own anarchic purposes, and then death would have to escort them all out. Sometimes death himself would turn frivolous and he and his half-sister would stage a performance – it was always called Romance. He would shed his servant's garb, and she would wash herself and tie back her hair in a semblance of innocence, and they would dance together. It was very dangerous, that dance. People should stand well clear.

'Sylvie,' said Claudia.

'Mm?'

23

'What are you thinking about?'

'I think I'm getting religious,' said Sylvie.

Claudia frowned. 'That's what I said and you said you weren't.'

'You said I was moral,' corrected Sylvie. 'The two things are quite different.'

'That's what I just said,' protested Claudia bemusedly.

'That was about sex and death,' said Sylvie. 'I was just thinking how incestuous they are.'

Claudia knelt before the fire and turned her face to its reflecting warmth. Sylvie *was* a witch. She should have remembered.

4

'Charles,' said Claudia that evening, 'I have to go to London and I may as well go tomorrow. I have to think about Christmas so I'll spend the day in Harrods.'

'Why do you have to go to Harrods to think about Christmas?' asked Philip idly.

'Don't be silly,' said Claudia, pleased to be teased. 'I must start getting the presents.' She did, in fact, regard Harrods rather as a believer regards church. She went when something good had happened, to celebrate, and she went when something bad had happened, to comfort herself. She went regularly for reassurance about the immutability of things.

'It's a bit early to start thinking about Christmas, isn't it?' said Charles.

'You always say that,' said Claudia. 'Every year. You have no idea how much organisation is involved.'

Charles looked stubborn. 'You get about a dozen presents,' he said. 'I could do that in one morning.'

'Then why don't you?' said Claudia nastily. 'Why don't you go and spend a morning and do all the Christmas shopping?'

'I could easily,' said Charles, 'but I'm too busy. You've got nothing else to do.' The truth of this did nothing to mitigate Claudia's wrath.

'Actually I have to get hundreds of presents,' she said, 'for your family and my family and the staff at the works, and Edith and her family, and my friends, and the children and the children's friends ...'

'Oh, all right,' said Charles. 'Anyway, it doesn't matter.' His wife had changed recently. He had never bothered to dissimulate when he was annoyed with her, but previously she had always apologised for upsetting him, even when he was clearly in the wrong.

'I don't think I can remember a proper English Christmas,' said Philip pacifically, and Claudia regained her temper.

'We'll have a special one,' she promised, 'a truly special one for you.'

Philip smiled at her. 'You mustn't worry about me,' he said, 'I'm not sure that I'll be here.'

'You get a week off at Christmas,' said his father, 'like everyone else. So don't go too far.'

'Oh, you *must* be here,' cried Claudia brightly. 'You're part of the family now.'

*

As Claudia went round Harrods she kept hearing herself saying that, and every now and then little moans of anguish escaped her, causing her fellow shoppers to eye her nervously. Never in all her life had Claudia heard anyone say anything so stupid. For one thing Philip had been part of his father's family long before she was, and for another the last aspect of their relationship she wished to be emphasised was the familial one. Then, for a change, she would wonder where he was going for Christmas. Not, she was sure, to his mother. Claudia was beginning to realise how little she knew about him – his friends, his lovers. She closed her eyes tightly and moaned again. Then she tried to imagine Christmas without him and found the prospect so dull and flavourless that she almost left Harrods without ordering anything. It was only the thought of the children that kept her walking the carpeted miles, buying them books and clothes with far less thoughtful care than usual.

If I was a proper stepmother, she told herself wildly, I could ask him everything about himself. But I can't, I can't. She couldn't even think what to get him for Christmas.

In the food halls she looked despairingly at the acres of infinitely varied and merrily packaged things and decided that, at the last minute, she would order two dozen small hampers and give one to each person on her list. Never had she been so lazy and impersonal about presents.

In the cosmetic department exquisite creatures offered to rejuvenate her hair and her skin and her eyelashes but she turned them all down. She was too unhappy to be beautiful.

She drifted aimlessly round the china and glass departments among strange desert people in robes and hawklike masks, and thought how it might relieve her feelings to push over the cabinets and overturn the tables laden with glittering, brittle things that would break. She wanted to astonish the dignified, far-travelled nomads with the quality and power of her suffering, but there were English people in the shop too and they would merely think her potty.

By the law of averages, there were in the milling crowds one or two tall young men with black, black hair; so once or twice Claudia's heart stopped. Black as the raven's wing, she muttered, thinking of beastly Amaryllis. She wished passionately that she could be the author of her own life, go back fifteen years and cross out Charles. No, not cross him out; she was very fond of Charles; just marry his son instead of him. Make Philip older because you couldn't marry boys of ten. Make herself younger; cross out Philip's mother while she was at it because she couldn't imagine any circumstances in which she might find Philip's mother a good thing; and generally tidy up all the loose ends. Claudia thought she could have written herself a much better script than God seemed to be doing. Such thoughts are known as *hubris* and are, on the whole, unwise.

At half past twelve she wondered briefly whether she should drop in on one of her London friends for lunch. There was a very hospitable publisher she knew who more or less kept open house, but his wife wrote books too and Claudia was frightened that she might put her in one, so she bought herself a superior Harrods sausage roll and ate that. She wasn't at all hungry, but at lunch time shoppers had lunch. So she did.

At two o'clock she bought herself a dress, a flowing silken dress reminiscent of the robes of the desert people. It was soft and black, like night, and very expensive and it made her feel better, so she went back to the food halls and bought a game pie for supper. This in turn gave her a sense of achievement and purpose, so she went upstairs again and bought a bright red woollen frock.

*

On the train to Oxford Claudia held the pie carefully on her knee planning what should accompany it on its last journey down Philip's throat. Baked potatoes and green salad, and marrow and ginger chutney. Philip liked chutney. She stared out at the passing darkness and thought of herself in the dark dress, her pale hair gleaming above it and her pale narrow feet below. Philip was much taller than she was.

She took a taxi to the printing works and went into the office to find Charles. He was standing, talking to a stranger.

'Where's Philip?' asked Claudia after some how-do-you-dos.

'He's gone out to dinner,' said Charles and, turning to the stranger: 'We want an 80 gram paper, but it depends on the price per ton. Send me some estimates for different quantities, and we'll be in touch.'

Among the photographs of herself and her children on Charles' desk was a copy of an Elizabethan miniature portraying a dark young man against a curtain of fire. He was very lovely, quite aware of this, and he looked just like Philip.

'The young man in flames looks like Philip,' said Claudia, rather rudely because the stranger was leaving and was trying to say goodbye.

'Goodbye,' said Charles. 'Well, of course it does,' he said to Claudia irritably. 'Why do you suppose I've got it there?'

Claudia had assumed that it was there by chance and was much surprised at this evidence in Charles of a previously unsuspected imaginative streak. It displeased her. Charles was good old Charles. She knew him well and did not want to have to re-evaluate him in the tiniest degree. There was enough change in her life already without having to cope with a new view of Charles. It would be as disconcerting as waking up to see a different landscape outside her window.

Claudia put the game pie on a chair and debated with herself whether she should sit on it. She hated it now that it had lost its *raison d'être*.

5

Evvie arrived again at supper time on Saturday. Tonight she wore baggy cotton trousers with a drawstring at the waist and a fairisle pullover; on her feet were green espadrilles. Claudia thought her very strange. Evvie was clearly not uninterested in clothes, since she had so many and changed so often, but Claudia had thought that an interest in clothes arose from a sense of style and taste and Evvie looked, if anything, even more peculiar than when she'd last seen her.

'How's the Scotch vet?' she asked, in order not to hear herself remarking on Evvie's ensemble.

'He fancies you,' said Evvie.

'You're not putting me in that novel, Evvie?' said Claudia, alarmed.

'No. I mean really him. The real Scotch vet.'

'But he doesn't know me,' said Claudia.

'He's *seen* you,' Evvie told her. 'He saw you in the baker's in a blue frock with flowers on, and he asked me who you were.'

'I haven't got a blue frock,' said Claudia. 'It must have been someone else.'

'Men are so vague about clothes,' observed Evvie. 'I know it was you. It sounded just like you. Perhaps you could have an affair with him and tell me all about it and I could write it down.'

'You have your own affair,' said Claudia.

'Not got the time,' cried Evvie, flinging herself into an

armchair. 'It takes me all the time I've got trooping back and forth with those dratted animals.'

'How is the poor cat?' asked Claudia.

'It's all right,' said Evvie. 'He poked the pellets out and gave it an injection, and while he was doing that I had a good snoop round. It's a very Scotch house – photographs and brass tables and ferns and things, and net curtains and three-piece suites and china.

'You might've been caught,' said Claudia, who could no more imagine snooping round someone else's house than she could imagine stealing their spoons.

'Then you just say you're looking for the lav,' explained Evvie. 'It's the one perfect excuse. I'm going to use it when I start on my next book. You know, the girl who's in fearful jeopardy and must on no account leave the room or the company of her fellows and she always goes off to get a book from the library or investigate a noise on the landing or something – well, no one in their right mind would do that if there was a maniacal murderer on the loose, but they'd go to the lav if it was that or wet themselves. Anyway, no one saw me.'

'I still have a strong feeling you're going to get into trouble,' said Claudia, though what she really felt was not that Evvie would, but that Evvie should. She reminded herself without quite formulating the thought that she was in no position to judge the actions of others and found the realisation unpleasant. 'I don't know where Charles and Philip are,' she said. 'They went off to the works first thing this morning and haven't come back. Are you starving?'

'Yes,' said Evvie.

So Claudia gave her a bowl of sorrel soup in the kitchen and listened to the story of the Scotch vet.

'In the waiting room,' began Evvie, 'there's a frightening picture of an awful-looking beach and a lot of sea, so I said to the housekeeper wasn't it pretty and where was it. And it's this fearful island where they come from and the wind blows all the time and there aren't any trees because the

Vikings chopped them all down to make boats and no one bothered to plant any more, and there's nothing in the village shop except knicker elastic and packets of pudding mix and wellies and one or two old brown bananas, and if you try to drive on a Sunday terrible huge men walk in front of you so you can't, and Fungus and Mango go flying round in boats catching millions of greasy mackerel and the fiasco stands by the stove madly cooking them all and Bridie keens awa' in the background and the sheep get foot rot and the staggers and their ears drop off and everything is pretty black ...'

'Did the housekeeper tell you all that?' asked Claudia.

'Well, no,' confessed Evvie. 'I just sort of gleaned it.'

'You mean you made it up,' said Claudia.

'Sort of,' said Evvie. 'Anyway, at this point along comes Amaryllis in the wolfskin coat with the loping wolfhound ...'

Claudia interrupted again. 'What's Amaryllis doing there? It doesn't sound her sort of place.' She was exasperated to find that these preposterous creatures of Evvie's imagination were becoming real to her.

'She's the Laird's cousin,' explained Evvie promptly. 'And she fascinates everyone in sight. Mango falls wildly in love with her and she leads him on because she's bored. Then she gets stuck on a rock all night in a compromising position with Fungus — they've gone to rescue the wolfhound or a sheep or something and the sea comes in — so Clara's heartbroken and Bridie broods and Mango does something dangerously self-destructive and Fungus curses the evil day she hove into view because, of course, he's fallen for her like a ton of bricks and he tries to deny it to himself because he's a decent enough bloke and he's promised his heart and hand to the fiasco, and all hell breaks loose,' concluded Evvie with satisfaction.

'But what happens?' urged Claudia. 'I thought these things were supposed to have a happy ending.'

'Not necessarily,' said Evvie. 'Not if I make it into a

saga. Sagas can be frightfully sad. But if I make it into a shortish novel it goes like this – Mango drives Amaryllis straight off the edge of the island into the raging waters of the insatiable sea, and Bridie bangs on about them being two lost children who were too bright and brilliant to live and now they're united in death in the Halls of the Sea King or the water kelpie or something – you know the sort of muck. And she stands on the seashore saying och a lot and wailing a bit because Mango was her ewe lamb in spite or because of being such a skunk, and Fungus comes to his senses and marries the fiasco and it all ends happily except the wolfhound sits on the seashore too while his canine heart slowly breaks. I expect Fungus shoots him.'

'It doesn't sound a particularly happy ending to me,' objected Claudia.

'Yes it is,' insisted Evvie. 'Boring old Clara gets the boring old vet, and bourgeois values triumph. It's what the readership demands.'

'Well, what happens if it's a saga?' asked Claudia.

'Oh *then* ...' began Evvie, but Charles and Philip came home. Evvie didn't like it when the men came home. She never had. In Evvie's view men were a nuisance with more or less nothing to be said for them.

She felt as though a large volume of cold water had been poured into a warm bath and rose to leave. 'I must go,' she said. 'I should go back to the vet's tomorrow. I haven't had a look at the bedrooms yet. I may have to shoot that cat myself.'

Claudia didn't say 'Evvie, you wouldn't,' because she thought it quite likely that she would. She said, 'Evvie, I don't know where you get your ruthlessness from.'

'It's the artistic temperament,' explained Evvie. 'The artist has to be ruthless in order to be truthful.'

'Oh, is that it,' said Claudia. 'I see.' She had meant to sound sardonic and was annoyed to hear she sounded respectful. 'Philip,' she added, 'take Evvie to her bike, will you.'

Evvie gazed up at Philip. 'You should've been here a couple of months ago,' she said. 'There were nightingales all over the place, yelling their heads off, and honeysuckle scrambling over everything. It was *so* romantic.'

Claudia looked swiftly at her, but Evvie was not being flirtatious. Her smile was small and indubitably hostile.

*

Sylvie sat on the step of her cottage, smoking. Light from the door behind her illuminated the greengage tree, from which leaves occasionally drifted. She was relieved that autumn was here again. Summer had always struck her as overdressed, making her wonder what it was that needed to be hidden. At the height of summer in the English countryside there was a blackness behind the sun, an old threat rippling unseen with the grasses. There were flies: flies who wished that she was dead, so that they might walk untrammelled in her eyes. Now with autumn the horror faded. There was nothing frightening in the bare branches and the stripped hedgerows. What had been concealed by riches was revealed by poverty to be non-existent.

She heard Evvie's bike stop at the bottom of the path and stubbed out her cigarette. Gloria growled.

'What have you done to Gloria, Evvie?' asked Sylvie. 'She seems to have gone off you.'

'I told the vet I thought she was going mad,' said Evvie. 'Perhaps she was eavesdropping. Talking of mad – Claudia seems a bit demented. She keeps doing that thing of going into the pantry and then coming out to ask what she went in there for.'

'Perhaps she's in love,' suggested Sylvie who had long ago discovered that the best way to hide something from the inquisitive is to stick it on an eminence and shine a light on it. People like her daughter only believed in secrets

34

– in what they could unearth for themselves from dark and dusty corners.

'She's not the type,' said Evvie decisively. 'Claudia's the sort of person who goes through life holding on to the sides.'

Sylvie smiled.

*

Later that night Sylvie thought about Claudia again. She had stayed up late more or less by accident. The fire was burning brightly and Gloria lay asleep, her head on Sylvie's foot. It didn't seem worth the trouble of moving to go to bed and Gloria was content to stay where she was until morning. That was what made her a good companion – she never tried to take charge in domestic matters, or fuss about the timing of things. She didn't even complain very much when her meals were late, assuming that, since they always had been, in the course of time they would again be put before her. It was trust, and Sylvie found it both flattering and consoling. Human beings had a nerve-wracking tendency to glance at their watches and exclaim at the lateness of the hour, or hold their stomachs, groaning with hunger on the stroke of one. It was soothing to live with a creature who neither nagged nor queried. It was this sense of peace which made her think of Claudia, for Claudia had lost hers. Nor, thought Sylvie, would Charles ever have permitted his wife to sit until daybreak, gazing at a dying fire. Early to bed and up betimes was Charles' rule, for there was work to be done. In Claudia's case there actually wasn't any work to be done, since she had Edith and, herself, no employment, but Charles would still expect her to be always in the right place at the right time doing the right thing. Sylvie wondered whether perhaps Claudia's beloved was rather like Gloria, easy-going and undemanding with the people he loved, or whether Claudia had done what so many people do and had fallen merely for another version of her husband.

6

Claudia lay in bed that night trying out the exercise known as 'pulling oneself together' and wondering who had first suggested that such a contortion was feasible. She was not unintelligent and she had been in love before and recovered. She remembered the happiness that resembles no other, of believing herself to be loved and also the sensations which commonly accompany it – principally a faintly sick uncertainty. Does he *truly* love me? Will he always? What was he doing at 2 a.m. yesterday when I rang and got no reply?

She remembered that these pains are frequently accompanied by a sort of impotent exasperation arising from the awareness that the object of all this passion is highly unlikely to be worthy of it. So to everything else is added the worrying suspicion that one has, in a sense, gone off one's head – that, even if not actually certifiable, one is without doubt making a great fool of oneself. The evidence is there, most marked in the attitude of one's friends. As for the eighteenth time the lover laboriously hauls the name of the beloved into, say, a discussion on the American Presidential election, and notes the expressions on their faces, ranging from puzzlement to pity with a clear element of boredom, she realises that they do not at all see him in the light in which she does. Astonished, she is forced to understand that not the whole world is in love with him.

Claudia repeated this thought to herself by way of comfort. She had developed a previously unexperienced loathing of young women. They seemed very threatening in their jeans and T-shirts wearing expressions at once beguiling and calculating. There was really nothing, she thought, quite as frightening as the young woman in search of a mate – ruthless, single-minded, seductive and proud. She admitted to herself that she encouraged Evvie because Evvie didn't seem to be searching for a mate. Claudia thought she would die if one of those predatory young beauties were to gain admission to her house, her life. Amaryllis, for instance. She *knew* she would die if Amaryllis should come stalking up the drive with her loping wolfhound.

*

It grew light and Claudia lay for a while watching a lot of very pointless birds taking off from the tree outside her window, flying round for a while and then returning to sit in its branches. Claudia couldn't imagine why they were doing it. She could think of no corresponding human activity. Such disorderliness worried her, but nevertheless she went downstairs in an old dressing-gown and without washing her face; which was most unusual behaviour for her.

'You ill?' enquired Charles in the way of a husband who loves his wife, desires her well-being but is – if the ailment be trivial – annoyed at the inconvenience her indisposition will cause him rather than deeply concerned at the minor threat to her health.

'No, I'm not,' snapped Claudia. 'I've been sleeping very badly recently. I think I might sleep in the studio for a while until I feel less tired.' She hadn't precisely planned to say that. It had been in her mind and now was out, and on the whole she was glad. She felt treacherous lying next to

Charles, thinking of someone else, and the fact that Philip's room was next door to the studio had not really been in her thoughts at all. Not at all.

Philip said: 'Then if you're awake I can come and talk to you and make cups of tea and we can laugh in the night.'

And Claudia said in a totally even voice: 'Yes, that would be nice.'

And Charles said: 'Well, you'd better laugh quietly because I don't want to be kept awake by you two hooting till morning.'

And Claudia who was now entirely happy said, rather wittily for her, that they could in that case confine themselves to smiling and if it was dark he wouldn't even be able to see them doing that.

*

Later that morning Claudia attempted to suppress her happiness, since she still thought that she must, in the end, demolish this unnatural passion, and she had not yet arrived at the next stage, which would involve rationalising and excusing it, with recourse to historical and literary precedent and much heart-searching as to the nature and meaning of primitive taboo. She went purposefully off to do the shopping, determined not to give in to desire and quite forgetting that the person who has just had a good meal is able to contemplate with equanimity the prospect of a long fast.

In the main street she saw a new man. He wore a Barbour jacket and gum boots and had the unnatural good looks of one of those martial dolls with which little boys play obsessively for about eleven months and then lose all interest in. Claudia knew at once that this must be the Scotch vet and watched as he traversed the road. She could quite see that he might be the hero of a tripey romance.

*

Sylvie pulled Gloria's ears and wished she could convey to Claudia the cure for love. It was marvellously simple, necessitating only the realisation that you can have anything you desire, providing you don't desire it too greatly. The successful hunter is the one who is not so hungry that she can't afford to exercise patience. The pursuer who is over-eager is incautious and her noisy leaps and bounds frighten the game. If Claudia could be brought to understand that, if she would sit quietly by her fire, bows and arrows out of sight, then sooner or later her prey would emerge from the undergrowth, unicorn-like, and lay his head in her lap, then not only would she feel satisfaction but much of the urgency would go from her longing. (Naturally the hunter must be wearing the right perfume and not have a face like an oil-rig, but given that, this is good advice.) Snapping teeth, gleaming claws and weapons alarm the timorous male – and rightly. No one wishes to be devoured – particularly not creatures who are themselves, by nature, predatory.

Sylvie wandered round her garden musing on love. The year was quietly dying. Leaves drifted unprotestingly from their source of life. The harvest had been gathered, and all sense of urgency had gone from the landscape. It was odd, thought Sylvie, that in what approximated to late middle age in the year, the earth should become fruitful, like Sarah the wife of Abraham. Perhaps if human beings were more like the earth and less like the animals they might die with similar grace. It seemed hard that women who delighted in fecundity should have to spend the latter half of a lifetime in barrenness. She believed that behind Claudia's passion lay, not the desire to be united eternally with her lover, but the longing for a child.

Still, smart as she was, she didn't put two and two together and come up with Philip.

7

The following Saturday Evvie came to supper again. Even Claudia could see that it wasn't because of Philip and thought it was probably because Evvie was, most of the time, hungry: she would eat left-over baked potatoes, the fat from other people's lamb chops, and cough sweets that she found in the kitchen drawer. It was quite possible that Sylvie never did any cooking these days. She certainly did very little during the week when Evvie was in Oxford, but lived on small things which had about them a natural solitariness – an egg, a tomato, a bun. Claudia, in her role of English Housewife, had often scolded her about it. Yet she herself seldom ate the same things at the same time as other people. When the children were small she had given them their breakfast after Charles had gone off to work. It had never seemed worth making any for herself since they left so much and it would have been wasteful not to use it up. So she had never felt hungry at lunch time. Then at tea time she would start to feel slightly faint and would have tea with the children. So then she never felt hungry at dinner time. The pattern had persisted. Except on very formal occasions she hardly ever sat at the table, but wandered about with platters and bowls of this and that. She felt odd sitting at the table with the others – as a corpse might feel sipping sherry at her own funeral.

Now Claudia prepared a large and nutritious meal of onion soup with floating bread and cheese, followed by steak and a salad of beans almost obscured by parsley.

'Cor yum,' said Evvie.

Claudia watched her with motherly benevolence. She had slept in the studio for two nights now. So far Philip had not come to laugh with her, but it was early days yet. The fact that she was not sleeping with Charles had also made her tender towards him and a pleasant atmosphere suffused the whole house. Claudia felt that everything held *promise*, and so she was not tormented by vain yearnings, nor yet by a violated conscience.

'I saw the Scotch vet the other day,' she said.

'Did you talk to him?' asked Evvie.

Claudia opened her mouth to say that of course she hadn't, and didn't go round accosting strange men in the street, and then had one of those dangerous inspirations that can cause so much trouble. She thought in a swift muddled sequence that she was in love, that no one must know with *whom* she was in love, that her overall demeanour might at any time make it clear that she *was* in love, and that it might be pretty clever to pretend she was in love with the Scotch vet.

'Well, yes,' she said, with what could only be described as a light laugh. 'We had a little chat about the weather and this and that.'

'I told you he fancied you,' said Evvie, chewing hot toasted cheese through a mouthful of hot onion soup. 'Ouch.' She swallowed and then gazed interestedly at Claudia. 'He looks a bit of a bounder, doesn't he?'

'No,' said Claudia, defensive of her new ersatz passion. 'I thought he was very nice.'

'He may be nice,' said Evvie, 'but he still looks a bounder. I cannot escape the feeling that some deity just knocked him and the rest together and popped them down here specially for me.'

'That's a remarkably solipsistic and self-centred view,' said Philip.

'Oh, shut up,' said Evvie.

'Tell me about the Scotch vet,' said Claudia with a

41

surreptitious eye on Philip. 'I mean the one in the book. Tell me what happens if it's a saga.'

'Right ...' said Evvie.

' "Nothing loath",' muttered Philip.

'Sshh,' said Claudia.

'In saga form,' began Evvie, 'Amaryllis marries Fungus and the Laird plays a part in the story. He's evil and twisted and drunk and queer, and all their lives he has loved only Amaryllis with a smouldering perverted passion. She's very fond of him because he's wicked like her, but she loves only the wolfhound. She's married Fungus simply because it'll make everyone so mad – her favourite thing is making people mad. Then the Laird marries Clara because he wants to spite Amaryllis and he tortures her with his unkindness and neglect and peculiar proclivities, and Amaryllis taunts her, and flaunts her power in front of her, and then Amaryllis gets pregnant – it's probably courtesy of Mango, by the way – and Mango's thoroughly cheesed off with everything and has gone to live in a state of concubinage with a fisher-lass in a tumbledown cottage by the sea ...'

Evvie paused. 'Are you following all this?' she asked.

'I think so,' said Claudia.

'Then just as Amaryllis's baby's due there's a shocking storm so they can't get to the mainland and Fungus has to get Clara to help him deliver it because Bridie's gone all to pieces, sitting by the fire with her apron over her head, saying weel awa' and stuff, and rocking back and forth. Then the baby's a girl and Amaryllis absolutely hates it, and the fisher-lass has a baby too and it's a boy, and by this time the Laird has held his nose and thought of Clark Gable and made Clara pregnant and she has a girl ... Can you see the possibilities?'

'I think so,' said Philip in his turn. 'It makes *Nightmare Abbey* sound rather dull.'

'All those babies give one scope for a second volume,' said Evvie. 'If I tried terribly hard I could make the second volume as interesting as the first. They usually aren't, because the author's used up her most fascinating characters in the first and can't think of any more. An awful lot of barrel-scraping goes on.'

*

Philip never came into the studio – neither by day nor by night – but as he was as attentive and affectionate as ever Claudia was able to persuade herself that she didn't mind. In a way she was glad. The longer their attachment just drifted on the longer would the confrontation be delayed, and Claudia somehow knew that confrontations commonly precede abrupt endings, rarely heralding a deepening experience. Once the cards were on the table the fat was in the fire.

Charles, having protested a little about the sleeping arrangements, now seemed resigned to them. Claudia believed that she had everything beautifully organised and was in complete control.

In truth Charles was far from resigned to anything. He was worried to death. He had almost, over the course of the years, forgotten the misery his first wife had caused him. After a few months of marriage Claudia had dropped the determined gaiety of the second wife, the insistent reminders that although things had gone wrong once she would prove that they could go right and, what's more, keep laughing. He had been very depressed during that period, infected by Claudia's submerged belief that only the first wife counted, that you could no more change her for another than change your mother. Once she had had her children Claudia behaved quite like a first wife. The trouble was that now she was behaving like *his* first wife. Charles knew that Claudia was in love as surely as if he'd caught her *in flagrante*.

*

So Charles went to see Sylvie.

Sylvie sighed when she saw him on her doorstep. She liked Charles. Although she found men alien she also found them capable of rousing her compassion. True, she suspected, Charles, unlike most women, believed in the vaginal orgasm while refusing to credit the existence of the Loch Ness monster – but then so did most men, in her experience. Sylvie knew at once what Charles wanted and how he would proceed.

'Come in,' she said. 'Have a drink. Sit down.' When she felt him put his arms round her as she poured out the gin she sighed again.

'Knock it off, do,' she said. 'There's a ducks.'

'You're a very attractive woman, Sylvie,' said Charles, stepping away from her.

'I know,' said Sylvie irritably. 'I know, I know.' Ever since she had divorced her husband and lived alone men who felt themselves to be in some way rejected had been coming to her, as though by right, for solace. Sylvie was perfectly aware that if women thought women who lived alone were witches men thought women who lived alone were tarts. Sometimes everyone thought they were both.

Charles, also, in making this approach considered himself to be acting chivalrously; indicating to Sylvie that she was still desirable.

Thinking of this Sylvie spoke more crossly than she might have done. 'Just give it up,' she said. 'What's the problem? Get it off your chest.'

After a number of false starts he managed to reveal what Sylvie knew already – that Claudia was in love with someone else.

'You got any idea who it is?' he asked.

'None at all,' said Sylvie, who didn't care either. The whole trivial business was so unnecessarily painful, and people in the toils of love so ridiculous, that she wondered how the human race continued. She didn't think the whole world loved a lover. She thought on the whole it averted its eyes from so unedifying a sight.

'She talks about this Scotch vet an awful lot,' said Charles. 'You met him?'

'No,' said Sylvie. 'I don't really believe in him. I think Evvie made him up. I'm sure Claudia only talks about him because Evvie goes on about him all the time.'

'Lives in that house beyond Bagley Woods,' said Charles.

'Well, if you're planning to go and knock his block off, I wouldn't,' said Sylvie. 'I'm absolutely certain from how Evvie describes him he isn't Claudia's cup of tea at all.'

'What is her cup of tea?' asked Charles. 'What more does she want?'

It was too late for Sylvie to insist that she didn't think Claudia *was* in love, even if she had been prepared to perjure herself, but she didn't want to be drawn into a discussion about what women want.

'What do *you* want, Sylvie?' enquired Charles with a mixture of gallantry and painful curiosity.

'Another gin,' said Sylvie shortly, rising to her feet and pouring herself one. Charles had always disapproved of her. She wondered why he didn't seem to realise that she knew.

He was reluctant to leave, standing in the doorway holding her hand and looking at her with sad eyes.

Oh, for goodness sake, said Sylvie to herself.

'Goodnight Charles,' she said aloud and closed the door behind him.

*

It seemed to Sylvie that in the unremitting dissension between the sexes, despite the current mood of passionate sympathy for the poor down-trodden female, it was the male who really summoned forth the tears – albeit sometimes tears of mirth.

45

Charles had been fooled by his first wife. It had been as clear as day to everyone in the world that she was the most promiscuous person since the Empress Theodora who had done all those funny things in the Forum: clear, that is, to everyone but Charles, who had persisted in regarding her as a dew-drenched milk-maid. This is known as the what's-a-nice-girl-like-you-doing-in-a-place-like-this syndrome, a remark guaranteed to leave the inhabitants of the brothel giving vent to shrieks of hilarity that would frizzle the ears off the departing male were he not oblivious to everything but his recent prowess. There is a curious flaw in masculine perception which prevents the approaching male from noticing that the ground around the pool has been trodden into mud by countless previous visitors. He tells himself that even if some other has briefly paddled in that pool, still, no one before himself has ever made waves. Sylvie thought that Charles's first wife had married him in surprise. Throughout the wedding Sylvie had thought that the bride's expression as she looked at the groom was one of incredulity. Charles had also, in a sense, been fooled by Claudia. True, she had certainly been of the milk-maid sort and she had loved Charles, but even as he had pranced about in triumph on his dung-heap she had turned away and was thinking only of laying eggs – which was really all she had come for. It was very difficult to distinguish the victim from the victor in this game since the participants were playing by different rules and had quite different hopes for the outcome.

Sylvie had run out of tonic, so she put some blackcurrant juice in her gin and stirred it with a knife-handle. It was peculiarly disgusting.

When she had forced it down it occurred to her that Charles had about him an innocence, a dignity, which contrasted favourably with Claudia's sly and feverish mien. Sylvie was beginning to take sides, and honesty was forcing her into the ranks of the enemy. Dear me.

8

Charles had left a half-empty packet of cigars. Claudia found them the next day when she came to see Sylvie. 'I didn't know you smoked these,' she said.

'I do sometimes,' said Sylvie, 'just one after dinner now and then.' She knew Charles hadn't told Claudia he'd been to see her and wondered who, precisely, she was protecting by keeping silent on the matter. What she didn't know was that Philip had a liking for his father's cigars and usually had one or two about him.

'I think women look absolutely *ghastly* smoking cigars,' said Claudia. 'I don't know why you don't take to a pipe and be done with it.'

Sylvie thought Claudia must still be more emotionally involved with her husband than she'd realised. Why else would her eyes have gone little and black with suspicion? It was all most annoying and there was nothing she could say or do to clarify things.

'I'm just going off to gather kindling,' she said uninvitingly.

'You're so *witchy*, Sylvie,' said Claudia. 'That's just what old women do in fairy stories – go round the forests gathering faggots.'

'Well, presumably they're concerned to keep the home fires burning,' said Sylvie, getting very fed up with the Bohannons. 'And that's what I'm going to do, so if you find it too sinister maybe you'd better go home.'

Instantly Claudia was sorry. She'd been quite spiteful enough for one day, and anyway she'd realised that it was most improbable that Philip had been clandestinely visiting her dearest friend. Nor did she want to go home, because it was one of Edith's days for cleaning and Claudia was frightened of the working classes, in rather the same way that she was frightened of wasps and cows. She couldn't understand their thought processes or why they behaved as they did. She often reminded herself that they were probably more frightened of her than she was of them, but she was not convinced. There was something in Edith's attitude to her that resembled contempt, that reminded her of the way the cows in their fields would watch her pass – unimpressed, chewing thoughtfully, unsmiling – and there was something about Edith's way with the housework that was peculiarly wasp-like, at once recollected and threatening. Claudia always felt it advisable to keep out of Edith's way as she buzzed about with mop and duster intent on her own pursuits.

She said cajolingly: 'I'll help you gather twigs.'

'You're not dressed for twig-gathering,' said Sylvie.

Claudia was surprised and glanced down at herself, her soft tweed skirt and her long boots.

'Real twig-gatherers like me wear horrid old trousers and wellies,' said Sylvie.

Claudia was dressed for a fantasy countryside – a fantasy autumn of crackling flame-like leaves and distant bonfires with crackling leaf-like flames.

'Oh, all right, come on,' said Sylvie. 'You can stick to the rides and pick up fir cones while I fight my way through the brakes and thickets.' She knew Claudia wouldn't stay long – she'd get tired of gathering kindling and she had dinner to prepare. 'You look pretty,' she added, 'but just a bit impractical.'

'Am I pretty?' asked Claudia with such fearful doubt in her voice that Sylvie was shocked into looking at her to check. She had always accepted that Claudia was

48

beautiful and for years simply hadn't bothered to ascertain.

'Yes,' she said. 'You're pretty.'

'I'm getting old,' said Claudia, and now her voice was full of despair.

'You're not exactly senescent,' said Sylvie, 'for God's sake.' But she remembered a party years ago when she had chanced to see Claudia entering the room. Claudia had come in alone and her beauty had presented itself as humility. There had been no sign of arrogance, aggression or even of much animation. She had simply come in very quietly as though offering herself up as a sacrifice, and Sylvie had been inclined to weep for her because Claudia had made her think of turkeys. Uniquely in the animal kingdom the turkey has but one purpose – to end stripped of its feathers, dressed for the table hanging upside down from the poulterer's hook. No one keeps the turkey for its intelligence or its charm or its way with the children. Few people would recognise a live turkey in a natural habitat. The sole point of the turkey is to please the palate. For a moment Claudia had seemed quite as simple, doomed and sad.

'Do you know what I used to think?' said Claudia. 'I used to think it would serve the world right when I wasn't beautiful any more. When people kept breathing on me and grabbing at me I used to think how sad it would be for them when I was old and ugly, and it used to make me laugh. It seems silly now when I think of it, but I used to get so sick of being loved. I sometimes used to think I was being loved to death. It never occurred to me that I'd mind not being beautiful any more.'

Sylvie was greatly surprised to hear this and accused herself of intellectual pride and insensitivity. Never had she suspected Claudia of introspection, never had she imagined that her friend was anything much more than a pretty face. 'I think you'll always be beautiful,' she said kindly, 'even when you're a million.'

'I don't want to be beautiful like that,' said Claudia with miserable intensity. 'I want to be beautiful for *him*.'

'Well, you are,' said Sylvie – thinking, 'Oh, my God we're going round in circles, as is usual when obsession has the chair.' Claudia would speak to her of nothing else until this passion had run its course.

'I keep thinking of all the girls his own age,' cried Claudia. 'There are thousands of them and I'd like to kill them all.' She looked as though she were about to cry.

Sylvie wondered why this emotion was called 'love'. Could it be described as *love* which brought the lover to a pitch where she would rather see the beloved dead in the gutter than blissful in the arms of another? It seemed to Sylvie to have very little in common with the tender care that the mother feels for her child, the trusting affection of the child for the parent, the saint's adoration of God, the creator's compassion for his creation. It looked to her far more like the emotion the diner feels for the dinner. As she was perplexing herself about this in genuine wonder she had noticed only the quality of Claudia's utterance and not its content.

Claudia, however, heard her words ringing round the rides, the birds repeat them from the trees, the groves echo them. Desperately she strove to gauge the years of the Scotch vet.

'He's not much younger than me,' she said, 'only it's so unfair that men can go on and on with young women and women can't have young men.'

'They can,' said Sylvie promptly, and she named two of their friends in London who were quite worn out with being pursued by what they described as 'babies'. 'It's epidemic,' she said. 'Old ladies and little lads.'

'That's London,' said Claudia drearily, exhausted with the frustration of not being permitted to scream that not merely was her darling younger than she but well within the Table of Affinities too.

'I always think of London as being rather pure,' said

Sylvie. 'Much funnier things go on in the country. Bestiality, incest ...'

'Yes, I know,' said Claudia abruptly. 'Can we go back now?'

*

'Mungo gripped the tiller passionately and turned the frail craft into the full force of the ferocious gale ...' Evvie said that several times aloud. It was very difficult. She changed 'ferocious' to 'terrible'. Mungo was in a bad mood again. He really did have a foul disposition. She filled the cleft in his chin with icy sea water to cool him down a bit, and headed his boat into the fearful trough of a vast grey breaker. 'The tiny bark was tossed remorselessly in the fierce rage of the dark sea. The bleak wind blew unrelentingly down the back of his neck ...' Evvie reflected that Amaryllis would find these weather conditions no end of a lark and put her leaning against a rail at the blunt end, laughing her head off. The poor old wolfhound was there too. He was probably being sick over the side, thought Evvie pityingly. She decided to keep the boat afloat for his sake, putting away with some regret a moving drowning scene in which Mungo and Amaryllis declared their undying love for each other before sinking for ever beneath the horrible waves of the relentless ocean. Anyway it would be pretty hard to make speeches at any length if their mouths were full of salty water and the wind was roaring like that.

Evvie was supposed to be writing about sincerity in Roman poetry. She wrote: 'Away to the north the thunder growled as though some vast slumbering beast had stirred in its slumber ...' She crossed out the word 'slumber' and tried 'sleep'. Then she crossed out the word 'in' and the word 'sleep' and wrote 'porridge'. 'Sod it,' she said, throwing down her pen and leaning back in her chair. 'She stared with unseeing eyes,' announced Evvie to the ceiling. She was beginning to think that every concept capable of

51

expression in the English tongue had long since taken cliché form. She had no objection at all to writing in clichés, but she disliked it when her thoughts emerged that way. Nor had she the remotest idea of what climatic conditions prevailed in the Western Isles – a lot of rain certainly, but was it commonly accompanied by thunder? Evvie knew that she could write the most appalling rubbish about human relationships, but should she get one geographical, geological or botanical fact wrong then people would blame her.

The vet's household would undoubtedly find it odd if she telephoned casually to enquire whether they had much thunder at home and at which seasons did it occur. On the other hand such a query could very easily be worked into a general conversation about the weather over the tea table.

Evvie donned her crash helmet and went off in search of some maimed bird or mammal. All along, the roads were floored with squashed things – flattened mats of hedgehog, torn linoleum of toad, ripped rugs of rabbit – all far beyond the vet's ministrations. Members of the scavenging crow family desultorily undertook from the hedgerows. Evvie made a few half-hearted attempts to run over one, but they were too clever for her. In the end she simply parked her bike, banged on the door, said she was passing, added that she was thirsty and asked for a drink of water.

9

'I stayed for supper,' Evvie told Claudia the following Saturday. 'They'd made *pâté*. I don't think I ever really knew the meaning of mortality until I tried the vet's *pâté*. It was grey and cold and flaccid and heavy and infinitely *dead*. Oh, it was horrible.'

'Perhaps he'd made it out of his failures on the operating table,' suggested Philip. He was standing behind Claudia, who was sitting on the sofa, and he rested one hand lightly on her shoulder. Claudia thought that she must look hugely complacent and at home in this position; that they must present all the appearance of a couple, and then remembered that when she'd had her first baby she had realised with astonishment that the perfect couple consisted of a mother and child and not, as she had always supposed, a man and woman. She wondered why she should remember that now. She didn't think of Philip as her son.

'Don't imagine I hadn't thought of that,' said Evvie darkly. 'Don't imagine I wasn't keeping an eye open for white mouse bones.'

'What do *they* think?' asked Claudia. 'They must wonder why on earth you drop in all the time.'

'They probably think I fancy Fungus,' said Evvie, howling with laughter at the mere thought. 'Come to think of it,' she said, 'the fiasco did give me one very cool and codlike glance.'

'You *will* get into trouble,' said Claudia. 'I know you will.'

'Fungus looked a bit fishy when I mentioned you,' said Evvie. 'I think you've been secretly meeting.'

'Don't be silly,' admonished Claudia with what she intended as an enigmatic smile.

'Anyway,' said Evvie, 'they're always very glad to see me, because they lead such dull lives. I bring them a little colour.'

'How do you know?' asked Claudia. 'They may have very exciting lives.'

'No they haven't,' said Evvie. 'They don't know anyone. Do you know anyone they know?'

'No-o,' said Claudia slowly.

'Except Fungus knows you, of course,' said Evvie.

'What's he doing with a fiancée?' asked Philip suddenly. 'I thought fiancées went out of style years ago. Has she got a ring? A solitaire diamond perhaps?' he enquired with distaste.

'I think they're still in style in the lower middle class,' said Evvie.

Claudia caught her breath. She belonged to that brief generation which hesitated to display its prejudices openly. 'I cannot believe the snobbishness of you two,' she said. 'I haven't heard anyone talk like that since I was a little girl.'

'Oh, come off it, Claudia,' said Evvie. 'You've met him. He's common.'

'Common is not a word I would use,' said Claudia.

'Only because you think it's common to say common,' said Evvie, giggling.

'I shall ask them all to dinner,' announced Claudia, 'and introduce them to some people.'

'You'll be sorry if you do,' said Evvie. 'They say some very peculiar things, and the fiasco says "pardon". I suppose it must be very coarsening to be a vet.'

'Of course it isn't coarsening,' protested Claudia.

'Yes it is,' said Evvie. 'They think about absolutely nothing but sex. Yeeak.'

'You talk as though sex was disgusting,' said Claudia.

'It is disgusting,' said Evvie serenely. 'I don't know why you bother to pretend that it isn't. It's stupid too. People who've got no soul listen to music all the time, and people who've got no brains think about sex all the time.'

'I'm ashamed of you,' said Claudia. And she was. She was shocked by Evvie's attitude to class and sex. She thought she'd been a rotten godmother, and she was depressed by this evidence of the retrograde aspects of the younger generation – especially by Philip's apparent concurrence in it. What really upset her was the indecent frankness of Evvie's admissions. Claudia had been bred in the ways of concealment. Just as she could not understand Evvie's mode of dress, so she was hopelessly confused by the cut of her mind. For years, perhaps since the beginning of the war, it had not been considered correct to talk about class. While everyone agreed that sex was no longer taboo, holding that death was now the forbidden topic, no one so much as admitted that class even existed, let alone that it was a fit subject for discussion. There had been a vague myth in vogue for decades that class barriers were disappearing, but they had merely been obscured for a time and had now re-emerged complete. The aristocracy was once more flexing its bun-flinging muscles and exercising its age-old prerogative of tipping the daughters of tradesmen out of rowing boats into rivers.

'Oh dear,' she said.

Philip sat beside her. 'You mustn't be sad,' he said. 'It spoils your face.'

Claudia smiled rather painfully. Philip liked beautiful things. He liked flowers and order. She'd watched him and she knew. She'd watched him rearranging the sea shells on a small table in the drawing-room, tweaking the roses into a more pleasing display, engrossed as the keeper of a virgin's shrine might be.

*

'Claudia,' called Evvie from the drawing room as Claudia prepared supper. 'What would Amaryllis wear apart from her wolfskin coat? She's a sort of nineteen-thirties-forties person. Very chic.'

'I thought your novel was set in the present day,' said Claudia from the kitchen.

'It is,' said Evvie, 'but there aren't any heroines now. Not real ones. Not wicked, spoilt, glamorous ones. They all keep *thinking* nowadays, and chasing after chaps, which is hopelessly unglamorous, and so she's got to be an anachronism.'

'Well, come here and I'll tell you. I can't keep shouting.'

'She's tall,' said Evvie, emerging in the kitchen, 'with straight black hair, and a tongue like a whiplash, and insanely lovely. An absolute cow.'

'She'd wear superbly tailored slacks,' said Claudia reflectively, 'and silk shirts, and grey flannel coats and skirts, and heavy satin in the evenings, slit up the thigh. And jodhpurs and soft leather boots ...' She paused and reached out for a knife. Between them they'd just more or less described Philip's mother. 'Do you remember Philip's mother?' she asked without thinking.

Evvie stared. 'No, of course I don't,' she said. 'She buggered off before I was born.'

'No, she didn't,' said Claudia. 'She was around for a few years.'

'Well, I don't remember her,' said Evvie. 'Why?'

'Nothing,' said Claudia. 'You just reminded me of something, that's all.'

'What's for supper?' asked Evvie. 'I feel a bit deranged spending all my time on that island.'

'I can see you might,' said Claudia.

*

Philip was planting bulbs for the springtime. Claudia found the sight reassuring. Being a woman she couldn't imagine starting something and not waiting to see it come to completion. Early in the year Philip would pick the narcissi and put them in bowls before the newly opened windows. The spring winds would stir the curtains and the house would smell of air and flowers. Already Claudia was weary of autumn and fearful of winter. She dreamed of lambs and primroses and a sky like a bird's egg. The sky today was like a tramp's overcoat, and the wind as piercing as a street trader's whistle.

Claudia put on her scarf and went out to watch Philip working. He was kneeling underneath a small tree; so small that Claudia had to bend, and one of its branches seized her scarf.

She waited for Philip to free her.

'What would you have done if I hadn't been here?' he asked. 'You might have hung from that tree for ever.'

But she wouldn't have been under the tree if Philip hadn't been there. Didn't he know that?

She said: 'How are you getting on?' Which is one of the better meaningless questions, since people seldom bother to answer it at any length.

'All right,' said Philip.

'I'll sit here and watch you work,' said Claudia.

They were still standing awkwardly among the bare constricting branches, and someone was waiting for something. Pride caused Claudia to move. There came a moment in waiting when dignity died, when patience became impotence. She sat on a bleached wooden bench a few feet away and watched, not Philip, but the sky. She knew what Philip looked like. She thought he was more beautiful than anyone she'd ever known; more beautiful than she herself had ever been. More beautiful than his mother. The wind had ceased to trouble her and she would have been content to die like the leaves, to be buried with the bulbs as long as she could stay with Philip.

'That's that, then,' said Philip, wiping his hands on his trousers, as people do when they've worked. 'I'm starving.'

Claudia got up, wishing that life was not so subject to swift change. Only the bad things seemed to last for any length of time. The good things instantly became memories, and ended shut away in drawers with the rose you'd worn at your first dance. Claudia was unusual in that she'd actually enjoyed her first dance, and had spent no more time in the powder room than she'd needed to powder her nose. It had ended too soon.

As she went into the house she thought that if Philip had gone away by the springtime then each green narcissus spear, as it grew, would pierce her heart, and she would have to go out and cut them all down. 'They give me hay-fever,' she would say, as Charles exclaimed at her vandalism. 'They smell so strong they make me ill.'

She removed her scarf and a nasty sense of grief and loss took its place, half choking her, and she had to remind herself that it was an idiotic waste of good time to spend it grieving that it couldn't last for ever. It was absurd to wish that this cold day could last for ever when she preferred the springtime. So everything was relative, thought Claudia, surprising herself. Heaven would not be heaven without the beloved, nor would hell be unpleasing if he was there. It was all too confusing. Claudia felt as she had felt when giving birth; that some power much greater than she possessed had taken her over and was having its way with her. Unwelcome as it was, there was no use in resenting it. Claudia felt like a Thing: depersonalised and, oddly, since it was her femaleness that was being exploited, unsexed.

Edith was wringing out the dishcloth with an air of finality. 'I've done all the bedrooms,' she announced with misplaced self-righteousness, since that was what she was paid for, 'and I've given the kitchen table a proper scrub!'

She had too. A revolting smell of bleach suffused the kitchen.

'Oh good,' said Claudia, feeling undeservedly useless.

She herself always kept the top of the kitchen table perfectly clean. 'Thank you, Edith.'

Edith seemed, for once, reluctant to leave. She looked from Claudia to Philip with animal-like inquisitiveness. 'Oh well,' she said at last, 'I'd better be off. Don't do anything I wouldn't do.'

'What do you imagine Edith wouldn't do?' asked Philip, amused.

'I have no idea,' said Claudia, humiliated beyond measure to realise that Edith, of all people, was aware of the sexual complexities that bedevilled her. No one else in her life, since they were all cultured thoughtful beings, would ever discern that she had sunk to a pig-like level of incestuous desire.

'Sausages,' she said abruptly. 'Bangers and mash for lunch. Will that do?' She had meant to prepare Swiss eggs or a soufflé omelette with asparagus, but not now. The time was past for erotic cooking. Edith had seen to that.

'You are clever, Claudia,' said Philip, lying back in the kitchen rocking-chair. 'I love sausage and mash before almost anything.'

*

Claudia, being sick with love, was drinking more than usual.

'You've been at my claret,' said Charles on Sunday evening.

'You've got bottles and bottles of it,' retorted Claudia, not defensively as she once might have done. 'I just had a glass at lunch because I was tired.'

'That's not the point,' said Charles. 'If you were tired you might just as well drink tonic wine.' Another of the things he believed was that decent wine was wasted on women, and in Claudia's case he was quite right. 'If you're so tired,' he said, 'you ought to see a doctor.'

'It's my *age*,' said Claudia loudly and suicidally because Philip was present.

Charles was bewildered. Claudia was ten years younger than he was and he wasn't tired. 'Don't be *ridiculous*,' he said.

'My poor old love,' said Philip in his open, affectionate fashion, putting an arm around her and laughing.

Claudia burst into tears. She clung to Philip and wept on his shoulder. He stroked her hair and then attempted to pass her to his father who, to give him his due, tried awkwardly to take her. But Claudia uttered a low scream of frustration. '*Men*,' she cried, and fled from the room. Her heels clattered up the stairs.

'Oh Lord,' said Charles tiredly. 'I've never known her like this. I don't understand.' He would say no more. He would no sooner discuss his wife with another man than he would try to sell her on a street corner.

'I'll take her a cup of tea and an aspirin,' said Philip, and Charles wondered whence he had gathered this expertise. So far as he knew Philip's mother had never wept a tear in her life, nor ever manifested anything but the most robust psychic and bodily health. He found women unfathomable. You gave them everything – love, loyalty, security, children, and either they ran off with a dago or they flopped round in hysterics, crying for the moon.

What more does she want, he asked himself, and then he went off and again asked Sylvie. He couldn't face another evening of watching Claudia surreptitiously helping herself to more whisky than was good for her, or giggling with Philip in the kitchen. He wished Philip would find himself a flat in Oxford. Charles loved all his children, but while Philip, grown up, was admittedly no trouble – certainly nothing like the two younger ones at home in the holidays – still, what Charles liked best was living alone with his wife in his own house. He wondered miserably whether that was very selfish of him.

'Philip,' he called, 'tell Claudia I've just gone down to the pub, will you?'

*

Charles fell over on the path to Sylvie's cottage, and Gloria, who performed the most important of husbandly functions, that of keeping away unwanted followers, roared out and barked at his head.

'Sylvie,' he said when he arrived at the door, dishevelled and undignified, 'that dog is dangerous.'

'I know,' said Sylvie, but she closed Gloria in the back room, where, after snarling and scratching for a while, she went to sleep.

'I'm really not the person to talk to about marriage,' said Sylvie. 'I was very bad at it and I didn't like it. I'm not very fond of men,' she added just in case Charles should be planning another seduction scene.

'Rubbish,' said Charles infuriatingly as though she had denigrated herself and he was concerned to refute her. 'Of course you are.' But he sat down sedately in the armchair Sylvie had been sitting in and accepted a glass of gin.

Sylvie sat on a stool near the fire. 'I'll tell you what I think,' she said chillingly. 'I think marriage is like a three-legged race with each participant harnessed to a loser.'

Charles didn't want to hear this either, so he didn't. 'You're wise, Sylvie,' he said. 'I've always valued your opinion.'

May you be forgiven, thought Sylvie. You frightful liar. She stared at him unsmiling. 'Or it's like chocolates,' she continued. 'The handsome and the privileged choose all the best ones – the coffee creams and the rum truffles – and the ugly little warts have to make do with what's left – the moth-eaten marzipan and the half-chewed brazil nut and the ginger whirl.' She had been so peaceful alone in the firelight with Gloria and the gin. She had had nothing to say and no inclination to speak to anyone, and now she would have to keep talking to this tedious man simply because silence was only acceptable in solitude. She was angry. Claudia's right, she thought, we are getting old. Once upon a time I'd have felt much sorrier for him. She reached for the gin bottle. 'Think of those people you see in restaurants,' she went on, 'the married ones who only open their mouths to shovel in steak. They never say a single word to each other.'

'But Claudia and I aren't like that,' protested Charles.

I bet you are, thought Sylvie. I bet Claudia hasn't said much to you except 'Pass the salt' for a good few years now. Nevertheless she was no longer angry. Charles looked and sounded hurt and Sylvie believed that the main purpose of humankind was to care for the sick and wounded. It was one of the reasons she lived alone, having grown weary of having this belief put to the test.

'I don't know why you say those things to me,' said Charles. 'Those things about marriage.'

'I told you I'm not the one to ask about marriage,' said Sylvie. 'I don't know anything about it. I find married people boring. I haven't got a single friend who's happily married. Happily married people are invisible to the outside world. They're incomplete, inaccessible. They're *halved*.'

'You've got Claudia,' said Charles. 'You're her best friend.'

Sylvie opened her mouth and then closed it again. She didn't want to say that she didn't regard Claudia as her best friend. Nor did she feel she could point out that Claudia, at present, was not happily married.

'Do you think I *should* talk to her?' asked Charles. 'Do you think I should talk to her about – well – everything?'

'No,' said Sylvie decisively. '*That* I do know. There are four topics which married people should never discuss – sex, money, politics and religion. Talk about those to anyone else you like, anywhere you like, but never within marriage. And certainly never discuss your marriage.'

'But shouldn't we just talk it over?' asked Charles, sounding pathetic.

'No,' said Sylvie, 'absolutely not. If you talk it over, that's exactly what it will be. Over. Why do you suppose there's so much divorce now? Because people suddenly got this mad idea that they should discuss everything. They find out all sorts of things about each other, and that puts them off totally and then they can never live together again. That's why the only ones who are still together are the utterly silent, bone-stupid ones eating their steak in restaurants.'

'That's a very unnatural view,' protested Charles.

'No, it isn't,' said Sylvie. 'People aren't very nice on the whole, and they do some terrible things, and the best course for them is to keep their mouths shut about it. And if they must confess, they should go to a priest. That's why priests always look so wan,' she finished, having grown tired of her argument.

'I never know when you're being serious, Sylvie,' said Charles. 'You remind me of Evvie. You're awfully alike.'

'Well, I'm her mother,' said Sylvie reasonably.

'And I'm Philip's father,' said Charles, 'but we're not alike in the slightest. It doesn't follow.'

*

'Oh Philip, I'm sorry,' said Claudia. She had come downstairs again and had lain on the sofa. 'And I've driven your poor father out. You must think I'm awful.' She knew she was still drunk and must take care of her words.

'I think you're lovely,' said Philip. 'I think you're the loveliest person in the world.'

Claudia lay very still.

'And my father's the luckiest man in the world to have you.'

To Claudia this did not sound insincere. It did not sound to her like the exaggerated expressions of esteem with which the good-hearted attempt to comfort the oppressed in spirit. Which only goes to show that you can't be too careful.

Philip went on. 'I adore my mother,' he said, 'but I'd hate to be married to her. When my grandfather was with BAOR they had to put her out of bounds to the British Army.' He sounded amused. 'She's still the same,' he said. 'She changes lovers like library books.'

'Don't you mind?' asked Claudia.

'No,' said Philip. 'She's been the same for as long as I can remember. There'd be no point in minding. She always saw that I was looked after.'

Then Claudia had her inspiration. It was so simple and so brilliant that she spilled her tea:

Philip was not his father's son. He was the child of one of his mother's lovers.

10

Sylvie had letters to write. She grimaced with guilt
whenever she remembered them, but the trouble involved
was too daunting. She would have to find writing paper,
then a pen, then an envelope. Then she would have to look
up addresses. A trip to the Post Office for a stamp would
become necessary: she would have to assemble all these
things and then remember to post them. And once the
recipients had read her letters they would promptly answer
them, and the whole business would begin again.

Sylvie had become extraordinarily lazy. Things bored
her. Clothes and cooking utensils and food and furniture
all bored her. Her house bored her, and she spent most of
her time in the garden. People, particularly, bored her.
She wanted only to stand in solitude and stare across
fields, listening to the silence. When she thought about it,
she knew that this longing to lie alone in a garden divested
of all possessions and free of all diversions was an
undisguised longing for death, for the final privacy of the
grave. That, she thought, was almost unforgiveably lazy.
She wasn't tired and she wasn't in pain. She was just
bored. Life was like a novel that she knew by heart: a novel
crammed with minor characters whose names she couldn't
remember and whose fates did not interest her. She wanted
to put it back on the shelf and turn to reality. Somewhere
outside this dreary book lay something of infinite interest,
and Sylvie was eager to discover it. For while the worms
toyed with her remains – and good luck to them, thought

Sylvie, since she cared as little for her outer form as for the clothes in her wardrobe, consumed by moth – she might wander, unhindered, in some other garden.

She grimaced with guilt again as she realised this. She had nothing to complain of, and Evvie surely needed her. Gloria certainly did, but Sylvie felt as she had felt when she last visited the theatre – a sense of horrid inevitability as she accepted that, come what may, she was stuck watching this tiresome pantomine until it was over.

She wondered whether Gloria's urge to bite the postman was a sympathetic expression of her own reluctance to accept the messages from the outer world that he bore. She could hardly bite him herself, no matter how unwelcome his official form as he stamped up the drive.

She hoped the day would pass free of messengers and mendicants.

*

Gloria brought Sylvie a present because she loved her and longed for her praise. She often did this. She would comb the environs for something good and dead, and bound up with it full of selfless generosity. Sylvie would thank her and then get rid of the offering in much the same way as she disposed of the tins of tea and talcum powder, sachets of pot pourri, and hand-knitted Tibetan gloves that came her way at Christmas and birthdays and now seemed to constitute most of the nation's commercial transactions.

Today Gloria had discovered something so foul, so indescribably unacceptable that Sylvie could find no words of condemnation, let alone appreciation. With two sticks she took the thing to the side of the compost heap, poured paraffin over it and set it alight. Gloria watched her intelligently through the reeking smoke.

'Make it a dozen red roses next time,' said Sylvie, but she admitted that it was difficult to choose the right presents. Very few people had the gift of knowing instinctively what gifts would be welcome. The kindest people were like Gloria and gave things that they themselves admired but would have preferred to keep and were then wounded when the recipients seemed insufficiently grateful; the rich never seemed to realise that what their poorer friends really wanted was a large cheque, and gave amusing token presents with expensive shiny bows on; and everyone else drifted despairingly into the Gift Departments of the large stores, or the handiest Hand Craft shop. There was a long daft tradition behind this ritual. Lovers had given gloves and carved wooden spoons to their dear ones over the centuries, children had toiled over unnecessary pen-wipers and kettle-holders for their fathers and mothers, parents had impoverished themselves to buy toys that would be forgotten by Epiphany. It was all part of the threadbare fabric of society, reflected Sylvie lazily, and without it the entire economic structure of the country would collapse. She regretted the disappearance of the profound and inventive spite which had once prompted the donation of white elephants. Creative malignancy had gone from giving, leaving it all rather dull.

The magnificence of 'half my kingdom and the hand of my daughter in marriage' had vanished from the scene. The words 'what is mine is yours' were seldom heard. It was the professions now which provided services and the practitioners merely took their fees. Charity had largely faded in the shadow of officialdom. Even Claudia, Sylvie suspected, had not given, but had lost her heart and wanted it back. The pattern of love changed with the years. Claudia had given herself wholeheartedly to Charles but the returns had been good. Illicit lovers had less to offer each other. Not really much at all.

*

Evvie telephoned her mother in a whining mood. 'M-u-umm,' she moaned.

'What now?' asked Sylvie grimly.

'It's that blasted cow,' said Evvie. 'It's got in my book and it won't get out.'

'What cow?' asked Sylvie, striving for patience.

'The vet's cow,' said Evvie. 'The one in his field. The jersey one. It's called Violet.'

'Well, I suggest you forget about cows and get on with Horace,' said Sylvie. It was the morning after her conversation with Charles, and Sylvie was out of sympathy with everyone.

'I've done Horace,' said Evvie untruthfully.

'Then be firm with the cow,' said Sylvie. 'Leave a gate open or something and let it get lost.'

'It won't go,' said Evvie. 'It's fallen in love with the vet.'

'Oh, *Evvie*,' said Sylvie.

'I know,' said Evvie, 'but it has. He artificially inseminated it and now it thinks it's married to him. There he was up to his armpit in the blooming thing, and it turned its melting brown eyes on him, and now it follows him everywhere.'

'I don't think that's how they do it,' said Sylvie doubtfully. 'I think they use an enormous syringe.'

'It doesn't matter how they do it,' protested Evvie. 'The result's the same. It got into the house three pages ago and lay on his bed. And what's more poor Clara is now in grave jeopardy because Violet absolutely *hates* her. Those jersey cows are the most dangerous sort – did you know?'

'Yes,' said Sylvie, 'I think I did know that. It was probably me who told you. But if you don't want the vet to marry the cow why did you make it up?'

'I didn't make it up,' said Evvie despairingly. 'How could I make up anything so footling. It just arrived in my head.'

'Maybe you should see a psychiatrist,' suggested Sylvie, wondering why Evvie wanted only to confide in her mother. Sylvie would have gone to the stake sooner than confide in hers.

68

She belonged to a generation of women who mostly did not at all care for their mothers. Even Claudia had been known to confess that she considered her own mother an absolute cow.

'You don't believe in psychiatrists,' said Evvie.

'No,' said Sylvie, 'but I'm beginning to wish I did. I've obviously brought you up very badly. Only very neurotic people write novels.'

'I know,' said Evvie. 'I'll give it up when I'm rich.'

But Sylvie didn't think she would. Evvie needed her island, her Utopia, for after all Utopias were not visions of the future but dreams of what might have been – the future being, by definition, death. Evvie clearly did not much care for reality; but then Sylvie wondered why when people insisted other people should face 'reality' they invariably meant something unpleasant. Either life was more dreadful than she herself had recognised, or there was such an innate pessimism in the human race that it clouded all vision. Perhaps most of the things that happened in the world were unbearable, but that didn't make the other things unreal. The hawthorn berries in the hedgerow existed just as surely as spilled blood. It was the fact of death that people couldn't bear. Frequently it was the prospect of death that drove people to suicide. Death was real, but whereas most people preferred not to think about it, Sylvie considered it a quite satisfactory conclusion to the bewildering vagaries of life. Even a sojourn in the flames of purgatory would bring you out cleansed, on the other side of the fire.

'Oh my Gawd,' said Sylvie, lighting a cigarette and wondering whether she was wrong. She admitted with unease that it was hardly normal to find everything boring.

11

One morning Philip told Claudia that he was going away for a few weeks. On a course. Claudia felt as though someone had hit her on the head.

'Charles, how could you,' she said. 'He's hardly settled in and you send him off on a course.'

'I didn't send him,' said Charles indignantly. 'It was his own idea.'

Philip smiled his beautiful patient smile, so Claudia knew it was true; otherwise she wouldn't have believed it.

'I'm going to the London College of Printing to do a course in computer-assisted type-setting,' he said.

'Sounds fascinating,' said Claudia, racked with jealousy. She would not have deserted Philip to study such matters. Perhaps he cared nothing for her after all.

'It's at the Elephant and Castle,' said Philip. 'My mother used to sing a rude song about the Elephant and Castle. You have to pronounce Castle "Carsole".'

'It's really the Infanta of Castile,' said Claudia frostily, thinking that this piece of information was very dull in comparison with Philip's mother's song. London was packed with girls. Girls to suit all tastes. Ones with pink hair and fish-net tights, ones with Liberty scarves and linen skirts. Big ones and little ones, fat ones and thin ones, clean ones and dirty ones.

'Where will you stay?' asked Claudia.

'With a friend of my mother's,' said Philip, 'in Kentish Town.'

'Is she nice?' enquired Claudia, picturing a gorgeous Socialite.

'It's a he,' said Philip.

'Married?' Claudia thought a married man might have scores of beautiful daughters.

'No,' said Philip, smiling, 'no, he's not married.'

The smile seemed to Claudia faintly knowing, as though Philip had been reading her mind. 'Well, I shall have a nice restful few weeks,' she cried with a merry laugh. 'One less to look after.'

'You must come up one day,' said Philip, 'and I'll take you to the theatre.'

*

Gloria had frightened the postman again. She had lain in wait for him on top of a low wall at the bottom of the path and when he parked his van and strode forward, whistling, she had leapt to her feet and barked in his ear. He had sworn at her and she had responded fervently. There had been several such unpleasant incidents. One day Gloria had taken a dislike to an apparently unexceptionable child in Faringdon and threatened to bite it. Sylvie had felt as guilty as if she herself had leapt snarling and slavering from the pavement to terrorise the poor thing. Its mother, understandably, had been very upset and had spoken of the police.

'Why do you do it, Gloria?' asked Sylvie. 'You know quite well that if you carry on like that I shall have to keep you tied up. Or, on the other hand, I may have you put down.'

Gloria lay on her back and waved her feet. Her ears lolled and her eyes filled with tears.

'Well, I will,' said Sylvie, 'you're more than an

embarrassment, you're a hazard.' The vet, according to Evvie, had diagnosed Gloria as half collie and half tan alsatian. It was, he'd said, an inflammable mixture. Whatever the reason, Gloria had made herself many enemies, and as is always the way in this situation they bracketed Sylvie with her pet, quite as though they were man and wife. If it went on, Sylvie knew she would have to terminate yet another relationship. 'You're a very stupid, self-destructive dog,' she said crossly. She much preferred Gloria to Gloria's enemies, but the world held that human beings must take precedence over animals and Sylvie was not prepared to argue about it.

*

'Amaryllis ...' wrote Evvie determinedly, pushing aside Horace with her foot, 'vaulted with gazelle-like grace over the low fence into the lush field. "Clara," she called mockingly, "have you seen my husband?" Clara turned slowly, feeling again the agony that seemed to seize her heart in a vice-like grip whenever she was reminded that Fergus belonged to another ...' Evvie sucked her pen, visualising this painful scene. She thought she should feel some compassion for Clara but could summon up only contempt. She wrote: 'Then Violet bounded out of a corner and jumped up and down on Clara till she was dead.' She crossed it out, and picked up Horace. Her novel was not going well. She thought all her characters except for Amaryllis and the Laird were twerps and was beginning to wonder whether, after all, she was not too clever to write nonsense. It was unfortunate that the subject of her essay was sincerity in Roman poetry. It made her exercise the higher regions of her mind when she wished only to wallow in the frivolous imaginings which emerged, when it was in the right mood, from her unconscious. Besides, when engaged on a work of calculated rubbish, the writer does not wish to ponder deeply on sincerity.

'The Victorians,' began Evvie, 'steeped as they were in the Romantic and evangelical movements, despised, because they did not understand, those arts of rhetoric that the eighteenth century had found congenial. To the Victorians sincerity rather than art was the hallmark of great poetry, just as belief, or at any rate agonising doubt, was the hallmark of religion. Than Virgil or Lucretius no poets were more sincere; and even such love-lorn elegists as Propertius and Catullus could be admired without restraint, for their agonies and ecstasies, however sordid, were clearly founded in experience and truth. But what of the faultless Ovid, apostle of pleasure and intrigue, who treated love and religion alike in the spirit of persiflage? What of that incomparable versifier Horace, who took to writing verses only as a last resort, for money, led on by "proud poverty", but whose Odes, as the critic complained, "afford no reason why we should believe that he was ever in love"?' Here Evvie added a footnote, giving the references in laborious detail. She went on: 'These are the poets who appeal to a modern taste, as they appealed to the mind of the eighteenth century; but to the Victorians, who were betwixt and between, they did not seem quite to reach up to that level of high seriousness at which art, religion and love were supposed to join forces.'

Evvie read over the paragraph thoughtfully, wondering whether she hadn't rather overdone the religious bit. After crossing out a few words, she turned with relief to her novel:

'Morning broke with a sullen gleam o'er the craggy battlements of the Laird's awe-inspiring castle. He awoke and called to his body-servant to bring him a pitcher of the peat-dark usquebaugh. A braw piper in kilt, plaid and bonnet prowled the dark mist below the bleak walls. The plaintive strains drifted up his hairy nostrils. The Laird flung up his embrasure and leaned out. "If you don't put a sock in it, Jock, I'm gonna take those pipes and push them ..." '

Evvie crossed out everything from the word 'drifted'. She had done a good day's work.

*

Sylvie was grooming Gloria in the garden. Gloria who loved being groomed didn't really deserve it since she had spent the morning eating the contents of the dustbin which was forbidden. As soon as she had finished the last egg-shell she had been seized by remorse and had gone away to hide, only emerging from the woods when Sylvie's voice calling her had ranged through most of the emotions from mild curiosity to panic. As usual when the prodigal dog reappeared Sylvie was so relieved that instead of administering the richly deserved damn good kick she fell over backwards being kind to her.

'It's a sign of extreme neurosis to go on eating-binges like that,' she said, having looked into the ravaged dustbin. 'Nice dogs don't do it. Nor do sane dogs. Only sick silly dogs, like you Gloria.' Gently she brushed the matted hair of Gloria's ears.

When she had finished Gloria looked very beautiful and lay back being *femme fatale*.

'I don't know why you bother doing that,' said Sylvie. 'You don't like dogs. Even when some handsome dog wants to play you just snap at him. I fear you're a dog-tease.'

Perhaps Gloria was like Claudia who even when not in love was always neatly turned out with her eye-shadow on and her stockings straight. Probably, conceded Sylvie, this was an admirable trait bearing witness to a proper pride in yourself; but it was odd, she thought, that she should see it manifested mainly in the two possibly least secure and self-satisfied creatures of her acquaintance.

12

On the morning of Philip's departure Claudia made him a special breakfast. Sometimes she felt that her only purpose was to feed people, like some stupid bird flying back and forth with worms. She often felt very birdish as she carried bag after bag of provisions from the car and piled them on the kitchen table.

She had made wholemeal rolls, and twenty-eight of them were baking in the Aga. There was honey and home-made strawberry jam on the table; there was muesli with lemon-soaked apple slices in it, and there were kippers.

'I can't eat that, little mother,' said Philip tenderly, and he had a slice of toast and a cup of black coffee.

Mother, thought Claudia, bitterly. *Mother ...*

Charles ate a lot of breakfast, so at least it didn't go to waste, and Claudia put the rest of the rolls in the freezer. At the beginning she had tried to give left-overs to Edith, but Edith despised her food; she carried on like Dracula at the merest mention of garlic and the only use she would allow to olive oil was to put it in her children's ears when they hurt. Sometimes when Claudia was preparing a little *boeuf en croute* or a *mousse de fois gras* Edith would clutch her throat and make strangled noises. It was terribly irritating – the more so since Claudia's sense of *noblesse oblige* forbade her to retaliate. Edith and her husband had awful rows about food. He insisted on three meals a day, each of which must contain meat and be bang on time. One Monday morning Edith had been in a foul mood because she had been busy painting the bathroom and had failed to make a complete Sunday lunch. Her husband had threatened to strike her, enquiring where was the Yorkshire pudding. Edith had retorted that you weren't supposed to have Yorkshire pudding with chicken (she had obviously gleaned this piece of arcane lore from Claudia, which made her attitude all the more maddening), and her husband had said Sunday wasn't Sunday without Yorkshire pudding – *and* mint sauce.

Once or twice Claudia had seen it as her duty to warn Edith of the dangers of animal fat and cholesterol, but Edith just thought she was cracked.

Now that Philip was going Claudia felt disinclined to cook very much or very interestingly. She remembered that, at base, Charles's appetites were not dissimilar from those of Edith's husband. He had spent his formative years in boarding schools and still retained a weakness for disgusting and unwholesome food. 'I don't know why I bother,' she said miserably.

Philip thought she was reproaching him for not eating up his breakfast, and he was penitent. 'I never eat when I'm travelling,' he explained, 'even when it's only from here to London.'

So then Claudia thought he was nervous, and she became anxious and over-solicitous.

They parted in a welter of misunderstanding.

*

The following Saturday Sylvie told Evvie that Gloria had to go back to the vet. She had fought the dog at the lodge, and had nearly caused a serious accident by rushing out and going bark-bark-bark at the passing traffic.

'You'll have to ask Claudia to take you in the car,' said Sylvie. 'I daren't risk a taxi. She's inclined to eat strangers, and anyway I think there are probably Wanted posters out on her all over Oxfordshire and Berkshire.'

'I can't take Claudia to the vet's house,' said Evvie.

'Violet would gore her. She's pathologically jealous of Fungus's women.'

'Evvie,' said Sylvie, 'you know perfectly well that Claudia is not one of the vet's women. And what is more, I'm becoming increasingly worried about your apparent inability to differentiate between *life* and your *novel*. I am getting very fraught. I have a mad dog, and now it appears I have a mad daughter too. What, I ask myself, have I done to deserve this?'

'Honestly, Mum,' said Evvie, 'it does happen. You can ask any novelist and they'll tell you. They write something and then it happens. They invent people absolutely out of their heads and then those people turn up on the doorstep.'

'But you don't really think the cow's going to chase Claudia?'

'I don't know, but I wouldn't take the chance. I'll make Charles drive us.'

'He'll like that,' said Sylvie. 'He's one of Gloria's hates.'

'Yes, but Charles is awfully brave,' said Evvie.

'I thought you didn't like him,' said Sylvie.

'I don't much,' said Evvie, 'but he is brave.'

'No wait,' said Sylvie suddenly. 'Wait a minute. You can't take Charles – *he* thinks Claudia fancies the vet.'

Evvie stared. 'The vet fancies *her*,' she said, 'but Claudia thinks he's common.'

'I wish you wouldn't talk like that,' said Sylvie. 'It's only affectation and it's very annoying. Claudia wouldn't say such a thing.'

'She didn't say it,' said Evvie, 'but it's what she thinks.'

'Anyway,' said Sylvie, 'it doesn't strike me as a good idea to take Charles there. I don't know how you've done it, Evvie, but you've managed to stir up a lot of trouble with your *magnum opus*.'

'It isn't my fault,' said Evvie, sounding injured. 'It's just that when the creative forces are at work a huge lot of psychic energy is released and sometimes it gets a bit out of hand.'

'Oh *nuts*, Evvie,' said Sylvie. 'You've been doing your artless prattle and that's what's got out of hand.'

'I have *not*,' said Evvie. 'I've never told Charles the vet fancies Claudia. I only told her.'

Sylvie was silent. She remembered now what Charles had said. He had said that Claudia talked a lot about the vet. At the time Sylvie had discounted this as a jealous inflation of the facts, now she wondered whether there was not something in it. Claudia was, after all, in love with someone. Maybe she was enamoured of the unlikely figure of the Scotch vet. 'Oh, bloody *hell*,' said Sylvie.

*

Evvie's feelings were hurt. She went upstairs to work on her manuscript. 'The mist hung like a pall over the island ...' she wrote. 'The lights of the humble crofters' cottages twinkled through the gloom. Mungo drove with reckless abandon along the narrow lanes thinking of his love in the arms of another. He drew back his lips in a savage snarl and slammed his foot down passionately on the accelerator. "Damn the witch," he whispered under his breath ...'

Evvie stared thoughtfully at the wall, wondering where on earth Mango was going in such a rage. Hardly down to the village shop for a packet of stamps, or off to tea at the Manse. The trouble with her island was that it was, of necessity, extremely low on civilised company. He'd have to be off to ravish the fisher-lass again, decided Evvie. He was always doing that. It was getting a bit boring, but there was nothing else *for* him to do. She made up her mind to set her next novel in some vast metropolis where there were places to go in the evening.

Determinedly, she wrote: 'Catriona looked up coyly from her trusty loom as she sat beside the sullenly smoking peat embers. The door burst open and there, filling the frame, stood the dark and swaying form of her lover. She laughed a low, inviting laugh and murmured, "Och weel, tae wha do I owe the honour?" Mungo came forward, slowly removing his dripping cape ...' Evvie turned back a page and mentioned that it had started to rain. '... Catriona slipped from her stool and provocatively undid the top button of her bodice ...' 'Hot stuff,' said Evvie aloud. 'I hope they both catch pneumonia.' She was getting tired of the constant mist and rain on the island, so she skipped a few months and brought winter upon them all. 'The strains of music drifted seductively over the barren moor as Fergus stumbled along clutching the dying sheep. Suddenly he came to the shore of the frozen loch. The dark clouds cleared and there before him, on the black ice in the pearly moonlight, was Amaryllis dancing alone to the ghostly music of a wind-up gramophone. She danced slowly with heart-breaking grace, her curtain of silken hair obscuring her pale, rapt face ...' 'Grace, face,' said Evvie irritably. She crossed out 'face' and wrote 'bum'. 'Slowly Fergus put down the sheep ...' Why, wondered Evvie, did everything happen slowly in romantic novels? If she'd written 'slowly' once she'd written it a million times. 'In a mad hurry Fergus flung down the sheep ...' That didn't work. 'With infinite care Fergus lay the gasping animal in the shadow of a whinbush. His wife was evil – but, oh, she was lovely, lovely ...' It was at this point that Evvie laughed until she nearly cried.

'What's so funny?' asked Sylvie curiously, peering in at her daughter.

'*Lerve*,' said Evvie. 'It makes me laugh.'

'It does me too,' said Sylvie worriedly, 'but I'm not at all sure that it should.' She was growing increasingly concerned about her daughter's similarity to herself. It had taken her years to become as she was, and Evvie was young. Evvie should be different, as she herself had been. Once Sylvie had thought that a version of heaven would consist of two or three days of passion with her lover: just long enough to drink a lot, eat a few meals of lobster, unborn lamb, nectarines and snow-cooled sorbet and to swear undying eternal love. She had never liked the idea of His and Her slippers and the Sunset Home, but she had had her fling.

*

The gamekeeper agreed to take Gloria to the vet, provided they made it worth his while. He had her measure. 'Get in the van, you nasty bitch,' he said. Gloria snarled, and then she growled, and then she tried to bite him; but he was used to coping with ferrets and poachers and was not intimidated.

'She just sat and sulked all the way there,' said Evvie later. 'She seemed quite normal, but when we arrived she was *dreadful*. She thought we were taking her to the gas chamber. I know she did. She frightened all the other animals in the place, and all the people, so there was a lot of barking and miaowing and swearing. Catface and Runt are usually very blasé but they both took off up trees, and Violet went and hid in the long grass. It took Mellors and me and two other people to get her into the surgery, and then several of us had to sit on her while the vet had a look at her backside. She didn't like that.'

'Oh lord,' said Sylvie, feeling guilty. 'I'm sorry, Evvie. I should've taken her myself, but I so hate scenes.'

'I quite like them,' said Evvie. 'Not so much at the time, but recollected in tranquillity. It's good material. Anyway, the vet asked me to his party after that. He said I should bring my friend. He meant Claudia. It's a Hallowe'en party.'

'That was very bold of him,' said Sylvie.

'He wants to meet people,' said Evvie. 'He's going off on his hols for a couple of weeks to look for some, but I don't suppose he'll find many. Anyway, he wants them here. He wants to be accepted in local society.'

'I hope you're not planning to ask him home,' said

Sylvie. 'He's probably perfectly nice, but you've managed to put me off him.'

'He looks all right,' said Evvie thoughtfully. 'It's the way he talks ...'

'A Glaswegian brogue?' enquired her mother.

'No, it's not that,' said Evvie. 'Actually they all do it. They say the first thing that comes into their heads. An idea pops into their head and a second later it pops out of their mouth undigested without a moment's thought, scrutiny or editing. I cannot *tell* you how disconcerting it is.'

'It should be rather charming,' said Sylvie. 'Spontaneous.' She watched her daughter curiously as she spoke. Evvie seemed quite unaware that she might have been describing herself.

'It isn't,' said Evvie. 'It's rather awful. It's what philosophers used to call "unstudied utterance", and you only really expect lunatics to do it. Not professional people who've passed exams. It's one of the things that makes me feel I made them up and if I'm not watching them they'll disappear. They're sort of one-dimensional. It gives me a terrible feeling of responsibility.'

'I wouldn't worry about it,' said Sylvie. 'I'm sure they exist quite well without you. No phantasm could have treated Gloria.'

'He's quite good with Gloria,' admitted Evvie. 'Doesn't stand any nonsense. I'm just going to have to be careful not to kill any of them off. I think it's going to have to be a saga. People don't die so soon in sagas, because you need them to keep the action going.'

Her mother eyed her. 'Do you really believe, Evvie,' she asked, 'that if you kill off one of your fictional characters its real-life counterpart will drop dead?'

'Yes,' said Evvie.

13

Claudia went stealthily into Philip's room. The house was empty. Charles had gone to work; it was not one of Edith's working days. Nevertheless Claudia carried a duster and a tin of furniture polish, which was a mistake because it made her feel both guilty and extremely vulnerable. It was the sort of error which a soldier might make who finds himself in enemy territory – for those who try to hide their identity and disguise the reason for their presence are liable to be shot as spies. No one would have questioned Claudia's right to enter any room in her own house. They would have assumed without further thought that the mistress was checking to make sure that the windows were closed, the beds aired, the dead flowers removed. Seeing her slinking uncharacteristically about with tins of furniture polish, their suspicions would have been aroused; they would have been jolted into awareness of her odd demeanour. What, they would have asked themselves, is Claudia doing polishing the furniture? *Edith* polishes the furniture.

Now, although there was no one present to see her, Claudia's pretence was self-defeating, and she no longer felt merely bereft, but also unworthy and sly. Notwithstanding, she looked through the chest of drawers and on to the bedside table for clues to Philip. There were none. No letters, no photographs, no nothing. She turned back the counterpane to see if a single hair, the hue of the raven's wing, lay on the pillow. It did not.

Claudia was beginning to feel insane, creeping on silent feet through her own house like a thief. It was *she* who had been stolen from. She missed Philip so badly that she looked up the timetable for the trains to London.

Like a compulsive eater who insists on having her jaws wired together, or the fridge door padlocked, she had forbidden herself to ask Philip for his London address and telephone number, and he had not volunteered them. It would have been the easiest thing in the world to say, 'Philip, where will you be if we need to get in touch with you?', but she couldn't. Her voice would have shaken. Now she saw herself at the Elephant and Castle waiting, waiting outside the London College of Printing, shivering in the cold fume-laden London air. She saw Philip walking through a columned portico, down a long flight of steps towards her. On his arm was a girl with hair as black as his own and eyes with the cold fire of emeralds. 'Aaaah,' she said in anguish, running to the telephone.

'Sylvie,' she said, 'I feel absolutely mad. I can't bear it. I miss him so much I could die.'

'I think you should treat this as an illness,' said Sylvie. 'I really do. I think you should lie down with a hot-water bottle and an aspirin and make people bring you things on a tray.'

'There's no one here,' said Claudia. 'Sylvie, tell me I mustn't go rushing after him.'

'You mustn't go rushing after him,' said Sylvie obligingly.

That wasn't what Claudia wanted to hear. 'What do you think would happen if I did?' she asked. 'He's so nice to me. I know he loves me. I can tell by the way he looks at me. You can always tell.'

'If that's the case,' said Sylvie, 'it's only a matter of time before he comes rushing after you, so I shouldn't worry.'

'But what if he's too honourable?' asked Claudia.

'They're *never* too honourable,' said Sylvie.

Claudia refused to believe that this was true. Sylvie

didn't know the facts. No well-brought-up young man would make love to someone he thought was his stepmother. Would he?

'Shall I come and see you?' she asked. 'I can't bear to be here by myself. I really do feel very mad.'

'Oh, all right,' said Sylvie ungraciously. 'I'll lock Gloria up.'

*

'I'm not frightened of Gloria,' said Claudia when she arrived. 'Let the poor thing out.'

'I'd better not,' said Sylvie. 'She's been very bad recently. She might not bite you, but she might.'

'Perhaps she's in love,' said Claudia morosely.

'Not Gloria,' said Sylvie. 'She can't stand male creatures. We're an entirely female community.'

Claudia found this impossible to comprehend, and could not imagine why Sylvie seemed so content..

'You are funny, Sylvie,' she said. 'How can you be happy ...?' She clearly meant 'How can you be happy without a man?', which Sylvie thought was a bit rich in view of Claudia's present state.

'Claudia,' she said, 'there's a very good case for saying 'Tis-better-never-to-have-loved-at-all than to go tottering through life with your nerves and your emotions in bleeding shreds. You cannot at this moment claim that you are *happy*.'

'Not at this moment, no,' agreed Claudia, 'but if things were different ...'

'For some people things never *are* different,' argued Sylvie. 'Some people can *only* have unhappy love affairs. Like some people can only travel facing the engine. It's very dangerous to believe that life itself depends on a perfect relationship with some man. The whole thing is largely myth. Half of it is engendered by women's magazines and the rest comes from male psychoanalysts

84

who believe that people who haven't got a what'sit can only be happy if they've got someone who's got one – if you follow me.'

But Claudia couldn't follow her. She had never really been able to follow her.

'Oh, I don't know,' said Sylvie. 'Don't listen to me. Perhaps I'm quite wrong. I worry sometimes that Evvie's so like me. Despite what I say, I sometimes wish she had a nice young man. I'm not consistent.'

'I was hoping she'd get off with Philip,' said Claudia mendaciously.

Sylvie glanced at her, surprised. 'Well, that certainly wouldn't work,' she said.

Claudia was too abstracted to ask her why.

*

Claudia only said one thing to Charles that night. Unhappiness had made her perceptive. She said: 'Sylvie treats that dog as though it was human, and Evvie treats her characters as though they were real.'

*

Evvie had definitely decided on the saga form. Apart from not wanting to kill off the vet or his household, she wanted to write about the Laird. 'He strode feverishly the wide length of the Great Hall. On the vast table the tall candles guttered fitfully in the icy draught that blew through the ancient arras ...' 'Cool it,' said Evvie, crossing out 'arras' and substituting 'broken panes in the mullioned windows'. She thought for a bit; then wrote: 'He glared wildly around until his eye fell on the regimental sword that hung above the massive fireplace ...' 'Dashed uncomfortable,' muttered Evvie, but she left it there. 'He groaned his teeth and ground ...' '*Bugger*,' said Evvie, altering the order of these words. '... at the thought of his love in the arms of another.' That wouldn't do. Every male on the island was working himself into a lather at the thought of Amaryllis in the arms of another. Maybe he was thinking about his tax returns. Evvie concentrated hard. '... at the thought of his proud, his lovely cousin, her wild, free, untamed spirit ...' Evvie stared at this plethora of epithets, wondering which to discard. She crossed out 'untamed', making a mental note to use it later. '... confined in the dreary, comfortless respectability of the vet's humble home.' He could talk about comfort, thought Evvie. There were dead bats in his own bedrooms, the mastiff had left its half-chewed mutton bones all over the Great Hall and the wind blew constantly down every passage and round every corner, carrying the stench of rotting venison. What's more, Evvie thought, there was probably a crazed manservant down in the kitchens, stoking the furnace with what was left of the Chippendale. ' "Clara," said the Laird, sneering evilly as he flung open her bedroom door and strode towards her with the lissom grace of a panther. Clara cowered in terror among the faded lace pillows of the huge four-poster bed ...' 'Oh, och and aye and haggis and hoffmagundy,' said Evvie, tired again of her inclement island and its disaffected inhabitants. She vowed never to be inveigled into reading her novel aloud. She knew she would have trouble with 'sneering evilly'. 'Sneeving eerily' had nothing like the same ring.

*

An idea conceived in drunkenness, considered in sobriety and found reasonable will, when the thinker is next drunk, have taken on something of the force of prophecy. This happened to Claudia. After a few vodkas it occurred to her that it was not only reasonable but inevitable that a person's putative stepmother, if she happened to be in London where that person was staying with strangers should call on him to make certain that all was well. It would seem unnatural were she not to do so.

The following morning as she examined this proposition she could find no flaw in it. That evening, after a few more vodkas, she made up her mind. 'Charles,' she said, 'I have to go to London tomorrow to pick up the things I ordered.'

'Why didn't you have them sent?' asked Charles.

Claudia displayed some irritation. She was in no mood to be questioned. 'I had things altered,' she said, sounding rather dangerous. 'I want to make sure they got them right – see?'

'Yes, yes, yes,' said Charles nervously, not looking at her. After a while he said: 'You might go and see Philip while you're there. Take him out to dinner. Cheer him up.' He knew Claudia had a strong sense of duty and would find it hard to refuse a call upon it. If she was spending the evening with Philip she couldn't spend it with her lover. He waited in suspense for her reply, pretending to be only half involved in this conversation, turning the pages of his newspaper. He was relieved when she responded mildly.

'I suppose it would be kind,' she said. 'I'll take him some clean shirts and socks. Men are hopeless on their own. I expect he's wearing the same ones all the time.'

This sounded so like his old, comfortable, comforting Claudia that he put down his paper and smiled at her with love.

She smiled back, awed at the turn things had taken. Charles had asked her to see Philip, and Claudia's reactions had become so stultified under the weight of her longing that by this she felt absolved from all guilt.

'Have you got his address?' she asked. It was probable that he hadn't. He left such things to her.

'Somewhere,' said Charles, feeling in his breast pocket. 'Yes, here it is ...'

14

Claudia had never been to Kentish Town before. She took
a taxi from Knightsbridge in the late afternoon, knowing
that Philip would probably not be back yet but unable to
wait any longer. She had planned to walk around for a
while in the streets where Philip walked, to see what he
had seen. It was beginning to grow dark as they drove with
many halts down the Hampstead Road in the rush hour.
Under the street lamps in Camden Town drunken men
lurched and stumbled among the shoppers. Claudia felt a
little afraid. It looked a very run-down district, ugly and
unkempt. Dark faces gleamed in the artificial light; bodies
misshapen by poverty and ignorance moved along the
filthy pavements. As they waited at the traffic lights in
Camden High Street she saw two of the fattest women she
had ever seen in her life – grossly, impossibly fat, as though
with a madness of the body. A boy with no legs sped
suddenly across the road on a wheeled plank, propelling
himself with his fists. Claudia wondered sickly why she
had never heard of this place, why it was not a national
scandal. She had had no idea that such deformity existed
in the pleasant isles of Britain. She said to herself, 'I have
led a very sheltered life', and half leaned forward to tell the
taxi-driver to turn round and take her swiftly to the
station, but she sat back reassured by his bearing. He
waited, quite relaxed, for the green light, unmoved by the
misery and squalor in the street. It's just me, thought

Claudia. I'm not used to it and I'm very silly and it can't be as bad as it seems.

'All right with you, lady?' enquired the driver, stopping half-way up Kentish Town Road, 'if I let you off here? That's the street. It's one-way. I can't turn round.'

'Yes, of course,' said Claudia, suddenly numb with terror and quite certain that the taxi-driver was refusing to go down Philip's street because it was too perilous. 'How much is that, please?'

Out of the taxi she felt better. She looked down Philip's street and saw little trees outside each house; and the houses were pretty: painted in baby colours – pink and blue and green and cream. Now that she was among them and could hear them talking she was no longer so afraid of the people. Many of them didn't look strange at all.

Claudia began to walk up Kentish Town Road, noticing with growing confidence that among the pubs and betting-shops there were bookshops and health shops and shops selling Swedish furniture – all perfectly ordinary. Boldly, she turned down a side street, planning to come to Philip's house by a devious route. If she took her time he would surely be home. She hadn't telephoned to tell him she was coming because she couldn't have borne to hear him say that he'd be out. It would be better to knock for ever at the door of an empty house than to hear his voice refusing her.

The side streets were deserted. No one had passed her for quite five minutes, and suddenly she was afraid again: not now of people, but of the strangeness of her surroundings. The main streets of London, the great shopping centres, the tourist haunts were open and guileless, frankly bent on commerce and communication. They had nothing to hide – quite the contrary, they insisted on revelation, welcoming strangers to examine all that they had to offer. The side streets were not like that, they had nothing to show the stranger. Closed, secret and indifferent, they existed only for their own inhabitants and cared nothing for outsiders. Claudia felt that she had intruded on someone else's dream and was walking, uninvited, in an alien mind.

There were lights in Philip's house. Her hand was shaking as she rang the bell.

After a minute an old man opened the door, an old man concave with ill health or alcoholism. He was wearing carpet slippers.

Claudia said – and her voice was too high and too clear: 'Is Philip in?'

The old man chuckled. 'Why yes,' he said. 'Yes, I suppose he is.' He stood aside, half bowing, and swept his hand before her. 'You must come in,' he said. 'It seems to be very cold out there.' Without raising his voice he called: 'Philip, you have a *lady*. A lady has come to see you.' He regarded her from her feet to her hair.

Claudia was trembling.

'How *very* cold you are,' said the old man gently. He closed the front door and again swept his hand before her in that artificial gesture, part servile, part chivalrous, and she went into a small sitting room.

'Claudia,' said Philip and she was horrified to see that he wasn't smiling.

'Your father said I must come and see you,' she said in that strange high voice.

Philip and the old man glanced at one another.

Claudia saw that still only the old man was smiling. It was not, she thought, a nice smile. 'He was worried about you,' she said absurdly. 'I brought you some clean socks and shirts.'

She was holding the carrier bags, unconscious of their weight. She had hardly even noticed them as she walked. No one offered to take them from her, and she began to put them on a low chair.

At this moment Philip changed, as though a puppet master had awakened from a doze and pulled his strings. 'You poor thing,' he said, taking the bags from her. 'You poor little thing. Frozen stiff and burdened down. Give me your coat and I'll fetch you a drink.'

Claudia stopped trembling. Philip seemed at home here. It was as though it was his own house. She too began to feel at home.

The old man made the drinks, and he made them very strong – so strong that after two of them Claudia felt more than at home; she felt that she should take charge in this masculine household since, in her experience, men were incapable of the simplest domestic tasks. 'Shall I make some supper?' she asked. 'Have you got any eggs and onions? I could make a soufflé.'

Philip looked at his feet.

Claudia looked at them too. Even as she had spoken she had become aware that around the small house there hung a smell of roasting beef and herbs.

'How sweet you are,' said the smiling old man. 'But you mustn't worry. We have supper in hand.'

'Actually, we have some people coming,' said Philip, speaking to Claudia, but looking at the old man. He sounded not embarrassed but speculative.

'And how fortunate that Claudia has chanced to call,' said the old man. 'She will add grace to our evening.'

Claudia felt suddenly glad again that God had made her beautiful, as someone caught in an unforeseen storm might be glad that he had remembered to bring his umbrella. After her marriage she had thought it rather pointless to be beautiful. She had never imagined until recently that it would once more come in useful.

There were four guests, all male, and they arrived in pairs. First came two men with moustaches, who very much resembled each other; then another old man, accompanied by a young one.

Claudia, who had been rendered by love stupider than nature had intended her to be, thought them delightful because they were all so very kind to her. No one would permit her to lift a finger. They brought her drinks. They asked her questions and deferred to the opinions which she gave in reply. Even the twins with moustaches, who at first had talked only to each other, after a while addressed themselves to Claudia; and the young man, after the same space of time, sat at her feet and fingered the hem of her dress in an affectionate, humble way, rather as her children had done when they were small. Being the only woman present, Claudia felt as Daniel might have felt had he been thrust, not into a den of lions, but a congregation of large, loving pussy-cats. A strange environment, certainly, but not a threatening one. She had never felt more at home in her life, and she found it unprecedentedly pleasant to be cherished as these people were cherishing her. They gave her the finest cuts of the meat and deliberately chose for her the smallest, sweetest vegetables. Assiduously the young man replenished her plate with sauce, and when she put aside a tiny silver sliver of fat he took it in his fingers and ate it.

Philip, sitting opposite, said: 'You mustn't eat Claudia's food. I want her to be well nourished. We all need her.'

So Claudia patted the young man's shoulder and then put her hand on his knee, saying: 'It doesn't matter. I don't like fat. I'm only worried about all of you and your hearts.'

And the old man, her host, said: 'You mustn't worry about our hearts, my dear. They may not be *quite* in the right place, but they suffice.'

15

'I had a *lovely* time,' said Claudia to Sylvie. 'I was never so looked after ever before. Philip took me to the station in a taxi.' She wanted to add that in the taxi she had leaned against him and closed her eyes; but that would have sounded odd behaviour in a mother, even a stepmother, so she contented herself with observing that Philip was astonishingly nice, considering his upbringing, and that she had never met such kind and helpful people as his friends.

Sylvie was washing up some mugs, a cigarette held between her teeth so that she looked like a gangster's moll from many years back. 'That's the way it goes,' she said, rather unclearly because of the cigarette. 'They don't want a mother-figure to mother them. They want to mother a mother-figure. It's not the way people think it is. They want some nice old bird to give sweeties to.'

Claudia had no idea what Sylvie was talking about and could hardly hear her through the clenched-teeth delivery. She was thinking of how Philip had buttoned up her fur coat on the platform at Paddington, saying that she mustn't catch cold because what would they do then.

'The dinner was *wonderful*,' she said. 'I suppose it's true that when men bother to cook they do it better than women.'

'Nuts,' said Sylvie.

'No, but it was,' said Claudia. 'They had wonderful langoustine in wine and garlic, and roast beef and tiny little carrots in hollandaise and heavenly camembert.'

'Camembert isn't heavenly,' said Sylvie. 'It's just gone off. It's one of the putrid things people eat.'

Claudia smiled. 'I don't think you appreciate good food,' she said. 'I bet you had a boiled egg for supper.'

'I had a rather weary mackerel out of a tin, and it made me think of Evvie's damn vet,' said Sylvie. 'Gloria liked it though. The way she walloped it down I think she was thinking of the postman.'

'Is she getting better?' asked Claudia, putting memories aside for the moment.

'She's getting worse,' said Sylvie. 'Evvie says the vet says she needs barbiturates, but I don't like the idea. I'd rather give her gin.'

'And how is Evvie?' asked Claudia.

'Sylvie shrugged. 'You know Evvie,' she said. 'She's like that.'

'I wish she'd let me take her to London and buy her some clothes,' said Claudia, whom happiness had made expansive and generous.

'She likes those things she wears,' said Sylvie. 'She's got this very peculiar idea that she's more beautiful than she looks. Not that she thinks she's more beautiful than she is, just that she *is* more beautiful than is apparent.'

'She needs to learn about make-up,' offered Claudia, who was thoroughly baffled by her friend's last remark.

'No,' said Sylvie. 'It's not that simple. Sometimes Evvie worries me. She's so clever in one way, and so completely young and blind in others – like a new-born mouse. And then on top of all that she's so alarmingly self-sufficient.'

'They're all like that at that age,' said Claudia sagely.

'No, they aren't,' said Sylvie. 'Not like Evvie. I've never come across anyone like Evvie, except for me.'

'If she's as like you as you say,' said Claudia, 'surely you must understand her?'

'I do understand her. What I don't understand is *why* she's like me.' Sylvie stubbed out her cigarette and lit another. The remote, disinterested goodwill with which she herself habitually regarded the world had come after years of experience – experience of boredom and misery, bewilderment and anguish, and rather less happiness. About an average mixture, thought Sylvie, but it had moulded her as water moulds stone. Evvie, on the other hand, gave the impression that life and time flowed by without even wetting her, and yet was similarly moulded.

'Don't worry about it,' she said. 'It's just my present obsession. I may not even be asking the right questions. Tell me about your love affair. How's it going?'

'I think I'm getting over it,' said Claudia, lying in her teeth. Although she wished to discuss every expression on Philip's face, every inflexion of his voice, it was an urge she could suppress as long as he seemed to be loving her. Only if he grew cold would she be forced into anguished speech, seeking for comfort like one who has learned that her god is dead and the source of all joy dried up.

'Thank heaven for that,' said Sylvie.

'Was I boring you?' asked Claudia cheerfully.

'A bit,' said Sylvie.

*

' "Come awa' doon then ..." ' wrote Evvie. 'Oh, wha' hae and dinna and tea and supper and lunch,' she said, glaring at the words she had just written and cursing the day the Scotch had taken on this unlikely air of romanticism. It all dated back to Queen Victoria and her crush on that silly ghillie, and Evvie was finding it very inconvenient. She couldn't think of enough Scotch words to get the local colour across. 'And puir wee cowrin' tim'rous beastie to you,' she said, addressing the irresistible Mango, who was currently in the course of attempting to seduce Amaryllis. The few Scots such as the vet she'd come across weren't romantic at all. They were prosaic, not to say gothic, creatures, and she couldn't imagine them in amorous dalliance for a moment. She knew they said 'Eh Jimmy' a lot, but it was not a phrase that would add anything to a novel of passion and intrigue. 'A mischievous smile played about the corners of his finely-cut mouth ...' That sounded as though someone had gone for him with a broken bottle, but Evvie was past caring. ' ... as he beckoned Amaryllis to join him on the silver sand. "Come awa' doon," he called, "and I'll ha'e you in my arms." ' Not on your Nellie, thought Evvie, but she wrote: 'Amaryllis laughed recklessly down at him from where she stood on a craggy rock, the wind whipping at her silken dress to reveal her perfectly formed figure ...' Oh, that blithering wind, thought Evvie. It never let up for a second. It was driving her mad. It was a miracle the inhabitants of the island didn't all jump off into the sea like lemmings. ' "Come and get me," laughed Amaryllis mockingly. Mungo's confident smile faded, to be replaced by a black frown. No woman on earth could resist him. He would teach the witch a lesson. Purposefully he strode towards the glowering rock ...' 'Run, you silly cow,' said Evvie, but Amaryllis just seemed to be standing there, giggling a bit. 'Oh well, take your chances then,' said the author. ' "Mungo," breathed Amaryllis as he seized her in his strong virile grip. "Amaryllis," he gasped triumphantly as he felt her yielding lips surrender to his probing tongue ...' 'Oops,' said Evvie. These were the tricky aspects of the romantic novel. Explicit acts of carnal knowledge were not usual in the genre. Evvie brought down an early dusk with a thump and left them to it in a force-eight gale.

*

Sylvie always jumped when the telephone rang, as though an unseen lunatic had suddenly screamed in her ear. Consequently whenever she picked it up she sounded slightly hostile. 'Yes,' she said abruptly.

'Sylvie,' said Charles apologetically.

'Oh hi, Charles,' said Sylvie.

'I'm sorry to bother you,' he said. 'I just wondered what you thought of Claudia now.'

'Same as I've always thought,' said Sylvie repressively. She was feeling tired. A bird had awakened her early that morning going 'tweet' with a precise, almost donnish intonation, every consonant as clear as a bell or a dripping tap. She had gone into the garden wishing she could climb its tree and throttle it. Gloria had bounded vigorously about, sniffing at things that the night had left behind. All that animal vitality had made Sylvie feel out of tune with nature. Go to Africa, she'd advised the bird; and then she'd had to chase Gloria, who had raced off down the path, hell-bent on committing some shameful misdemeanour. Sylvie did not now wish to become involved in human relationships.

'Do you think she seems happier?' pleaded Charles.

'Yes, I think she does,' said Sylvie. 'I think she's getting over whatever it was.'

'So do I,' said Charles, sounding relieved. 'I just wanted to know what you thought.'

'That's what I think,' said Sylvie. 'I think she's getting better. Thirty all,' she added to herself.

'Yes, I think so too,' said Charles.

So we all think the same, mouthed Sylvie silently, gesturing at the air and rolling her eyes. She wondered how long Charles could sustain this conversation without introducing some new theme.

'I think she's much better,' said Charles.

'Yes, I think she is,' returned Sylvie. 'Deuce,' she said to herself.

'Well, I just wanted to know what you thought,' said Charles after a pause during which Sylvie had stared interestedly at the hand-set.

'I think the same as you think,' she said. 'Goodbye, Charles.'

'Goodbye, Sylvie,' he said reluctantly, and just as she hung up she heard him say, 'I think ...'

'Therefore you are,' said Sylvie to the silenced instrument. 'Game, set and match.' The telephone looked to her tired eyes faintly sullen as though it felt she didn't appreciate it sufficiently. Sometimes Gloria wore the same air, and so had her husband all those years ago.

I'm getting old, thought Sylvie. Can't do without my sleep. When she didn't sleep well she grew depressed, and when she was depressed things began to look odd to her. Very subtly their shapes would change, a hint of darkness would shadow and distort the most harmless everyday objects. She would turn, half expecting to see the armchair extending its arms to embrace her; she would look at the tea pot, wondering if it would raise its lid in tacit greeting.

'Perhaps we're alone too much,' she said to Gloria, who rose to her paws and approached her lovingly. 'Perhaps we should see more people. Perhaps you should see more dogs. But you wouldn't like that, would you? You're a killer at heart, aren't you? The vet said you were. He said if he met you in the street he'd know at once that you were a killer, you naughty thing.'

Gloria fawned on her, apparently enchanted with this assessment of her character.

'Silly bitch, you are,' said Sylvie fondly.

16

Two weeks had nearly passed. It was almost time for Philip to return. Claudia hummed soppy love songs as she moved around the house. She believed that during the course of the Kentish Town dinner their relationship had altered – that they had appeared in public as a couple and had been accepted. Nothing, she thought, would ever be the same again. Every day she re-lived the evening, remembering fragments of conversation. At one point one of the moustachioed twins had leant across to Philip and asked curiously, 'Is she yours?', and Philip had said, smiling, 'I'm not *legally* entitled to her, not really ...' Claudia shuddered when she remembered that. Amused, she realised that she had learnt none of the names of her fellow guests. She supposed that they had been told to her, but she had been so apprehensive at first that nothing had registered. She thought that introductions must have been made but could recall none of them. I was foolish, she thought, to have been so frightened.

*

That night Philip telephoned and spoke to Charles.

Charles came into the kitchen where Claudia was peeling onions and said: 'That was Philip.'

Claudia stopped doing what she was doing. 'Didn't he ask to speak to me?' she said.

'No,' said Charles, sounding faintly surprised at her

question. 'He's staying on in London. The chance of a course of some lectures came up, so he's staying.'

'These are terrible onions,' said Claudia with tears pouring down her cheeks. 'I don't know where they come from. I wish I'd remembered to put them in the fridge before I started peeling them. If you put them in the fridge they don't make you cry.'

'Poor old girl,' said Charles absently, patting her back. Usually when he called her 'old girl' Claudia felt inclined to take the meat cleaver to him, but tonight she wished she could turn to him and weep in his arms for a long time. But she was an honourable person and she knew, even in her misery, that it would not be seemly to weep in the arms of a man because she desired someone whom he believed to be his son, and her heart was broken.

Later that night, without saying a word, she returned to their bedroom. Charles found her there, asleep, and believed that all was now well.

*

The following morning Claudia was rude to Edith for the very first time.

Claudia had bought a frozen Shepherd's Pie for supper because she was too low to do anything else.

'Didn't know you ate things like that,' Edith said, poking it with a finger as she passed with her duster. She grinned with the contempt of a whore who sees the vicar's wife plying for trade on the same street corner as herself.

'We do eat Shepherd's Pie,' said Claudia, 'only we don't have oven chips and tinned peas with it. Nor tomato sauce,' she added as a sort of *coup de grace*.

Edith obviously understood that this was meant to be offensive and was duly offended. 'Frozen too,' she observed, curling her lip.

Claudia, who had already said more than enough, now merely thought about the times she'd met Edith staggering home from the frozen-food centre with sacks of snacks and pies and burgers and faggots and ices and mousses in suspended animation like things embalmed from the mortuary. She wondered whether she'd annoyed Edith sufficiently to make her give notice. She doubted it. Edith was an old hand at quarrelling and took it all in her stride.

Claudia lifted her long white scarf from the peg, found her car keys and went out without speaking. Normally she would have explained to Edith where she was going and, quite possibly, why. Edith was never at all interested, but it seemed discourteous simply to go silently from the house. Claudia always had a feeling that Edith might imagine she was going to a glamorous occasion to revel in champagne and strawberries leaving her poor cleaning lady up to the reddened elbows in dirty water. Actually Edith led a rich and varied social life with many holidays, trips and treats, and Claudia knew this perfectly well. She also knew that the wages she paid her made this possible; yet still, she could not get over a sense of guilty pity for her employee. Really, she felt sorry for Edith because Edith wasn't her – which was silly, considering the painful state of Claudia's emotions and the fact that Edith, although presently in a huff, was, on the whole, as merry as a cricket. If Claudia had only considered that, she might have felt less anxious. As it was, she got into her car, harrassed by a foreboding that was beginning to overshadow her misery. It was the fear of *nemesis*.

She drove for a while around Oxfordshire and Berkshire wondering where she was going. There were many people she could have called on – wives alone at home, retired gentlemen – but none of them knew how unhappy she was, so she would have either to dissemble or explain, and she knew she could do neither of these things. Philip was now beginning to seem unreal to her. The dead seemed closer and more immediate. It was as though he had never existed and she was in love with a chimaera. She could no longer believe that she would ever see him again. Sometimes when she thought of his cold cruelty in keeping himself from her, not speaking, not writing, she was briefly warmed by a shining anger, fuelled by pride, but the glow never lasted long because she would remember the way he looked at her and the things he said to her, and she would wonder what force it was that kept him from her.

*

'Oh blast,' said Sylvie as Gloria leapt, howling, at the door. 'Shut up, Gloria. It's probably the baker.'

It wasn't the baker. It was Claudia. (It would've been very boring of course if it had been the baker – 'Small white, small wholemeal and a couple of croissants'.)

Claudia had known for the last few miles that she was going, not home, but to see Sylvie. Sylvie had also known, with resignation, that Claudia was about due to turn up. So was Charles. She hoped they wouldn't turn up together. It would be embarrassing. She could almost hear herself saying, 'Oh, Claudia, do you remember Charles?', as one does when introducing people who do not wish to meet.

'Sorry, Sylvie,' said Claudia. 'I know you'd rather be by yourself, but I had to see you.' She did know this, finding it strange, but accepting it. 'Gloria, do stop,' she added, as Gloria barked neurotically at her from a corner.

'You're the only person I know, apart from Evvie, who isn't frightened of Gloria,' said Sylvie admiringly.

'I don't mind dogs,' said Claudia. 'Cows I mind.'

'Perhaps it's true that they don't bite people who aren't frightened of them,' said Sylvie. 'I never really believed it. Gloria usually wants to bite everyone. I think the whole world must go in terror of her.'

'She reminds me of Jack,' said Claudia. 'Jack was rude to everyone too.'

Jack was Sylvie's ex-husband and Claudia was quite right. 'You're absolutely right,' said Sylvie, recognising this. 'How awful. I must be the sort of person who prefers to live with a ravening tyrant.'

'I don't think she's as bad as Jack,' said Claudia. 'She doesn't say those things.' Jack had had a tongue that would slice raw meat.

'She's over-protective in exactly the same way,' said Sylvie. 'Once I spilled some man's beer by accident in the pub and he said "Oi, that's my beer", and Jack said, "Don't you say 'Oi' to my wife", and you can imagine the rest – whereas if he'd left it to me I'd have had that man buying me a brandy, because he'd have been so sorry for me spilling his beer.'

For some minutes they had discussed something other than Claudia's infatuation. Sylvie began to think that perhaps it was true that Claudia was recovering from her obsession, but then she noticed that she was looking very white, and after a moment Claudia asked, 'If they don't write to you or try and see you, does it mean they don't love you?'

This seemed to Sylvie self-evident, but you don't throw cold water over the victims of road accidents and Claudia looked hurt and shocked, so Sylvie said: 'Not necessarily. There could be reasons, I suppose.'

There was no real content to this aspirin-like statement, but Claudia looked a little more relaxed. 'I haven't seen him for some time, you see. And I haven't heard from him. But it isn't really so long, so I expect I'm just being silly.'

'Have a gin,' said Sylvie. 'Cheer you up. How's Philip?' she asked, by way of changing the subject.

'I think he's fine. We haven't heard from him for a few weeks either,' said Claudia with serpentine cunning. 'I rather miss him. I believe I'm getting as fond of him as I am of my own children.'

Sylvie did not recognise her own ploy of rendering the truth invisible. 'That's nice,' she said absently. Talking of Gloria had made her think of the vet, and thinking of the vet had reminded her that Evvie had said he was going away for a few weeks. Claudia had not seen her love for a few weeks. Ergo ...

'Is he a local person, your person?' she asked carefully.

'Not really,' said Claudia. 'I wish I could tell you who it is, but it wouldn't be fair.' This assigning to herself of a noble rather than an ignoble motive for her reticence made her feel worse. She thought it extraordinary that there was so much sin around when it made the perpetrator feel so ghastly.

'Claudia,' said Sylvie, looking at her friend's face. 'You mustn't mind so much. It'll go away in time. I don't know if you remember, but it does go away. You absolutely must hang on to your dignity. You absolutely mustn't lie down in the street in front of his house, or turn up at his place of work wringing your hands.'

'I know,' said Claudia, who had toyed with both these ideas.

'Dignity, I admit, will not keep you warm in winter, but it is a little something to cover the nakedness. You'll get over the love in time, but you'd never get over the shame of exposing yourself, any more than you'd ever get over being discovered racing round Faringdon in your pelt. You see, when people lose their hearts they frequently lose their minds too, retaining only their organs of generation. This is why love is such a sad, mad and chancy business.'

Claudia smiled. 'You looked so serious when you said that, Sylvie.'

'I am serious,' said Sylvie. 'Love is so akin to madness one can hardly tell them apart, and mad people are in the way of tearing off their clothes and making everyone shy.'

'I won't,' said Claudia. 'I might die, but I'll keep my clothes on – I promise.' She had another gin and then left.

Sylvie lay back in her chair and called her dog.

No dog.

'Gloria,' she said sharply, sitting up and staring about her. 'Where are you, you hell hound?'

She got up quickly and went to the door. 'Gloria,' she yelled. 'Oh Lord,' said Sylvie running down the path.

Claudia's car was at right-angles to the drive. It's front bumper was nuzzling a sapling and its bonnet was up. Sylvie could see no sign of life except for Gloria who was ambling towards her with a patently false air of insouciance.

'You *bloody* dog,' said Sylvie, her hair prickling with terror. 'You've gone and killed Claudia.'

'I'm all right,' said Claudia. She was sitting quite still, staring at the upright bonnet. That had been the worst bit. The sudden obliteration of all vision like the realisation of her foreboding. It had been as though a huge black bird of death had swept before her and darkened her eyes.

'Oh God,' said Sylvie, '*I'm* not all right. I think it's cardiac arrest. What happened?'

Claudia looked at her pensively. She felt perfectly calm. Whenever there was a car accident there was the possibility of death. She might have died. She wished she had. 'It was Gloria,' she said. 'She came haring along, leaping at the wheels, so I turned into the verge and the bonnet flew up. It was nothing really. I didn't want to run over her.'

'I wish you had,' said Sylvie, stiff with rage and fright. 'I wish you'd killed her.'

'I don't think anything's broken,' said Claudia, climbing out and pushing the bonnet down. 'I'll just back up and see if there's much wrong.' She was thinking that this mishap might have been a blessing in disguise. If she really couldn't hide her misery she could have a convulsive crying fit and explain that it was all due to shock.

'Do you think you should drive?' asked Sylvie, her hand on Gloria's collar in a stranglehold.

'I'm quite all right,' said Claudia softly. 'You mustn't worry '

17

'I hear Gloria nearly killed you,' said Evvie next time she turned up at Claudia's house.

'That's an exaggeration,' said Claudia. 'I just had to turn off the road.'

'Cars look funny turned off the road,' said Evvie. 'They should be *on* the road, facing up or down. When they're not, there's always something wrong.'

'That's true,' said Claudia without interest. Evvie was wearing a white embroidered dress. That was fine, but under it she wore frayed jeans, and over it she wore a padded cotton jacket. She didn't look quite so odd once she'd taken off her crash helmet, but she still looked fairly odd.

'I expect you're hungry,' said Claudia.

'I am rather,' said Evvie.

'I haven't got much in,' said Claudia. 'Charles is dining in Oxford tonight, so I wasn't going to bother. I've got bacon and eggs.'

Evvie looked disappointed. 'That'll be lovely,' she said.

Claudia, noting the look, felt compassion. 'I've got spinach too,' she said. 'You could have eggs on spinach and brown bread and butter *and* bacon.'

'*Yeah*,' said Evvie with enthusiasm.

'How's your novel?' asked Claudia, lifting the cover of the Aga.

'I'm stuck on the title now,' said Evvie. 'I was going to

call it The Passionate Isles, but then I got this image of a lot of amorous islands tossing around in the ocean like turtles. You'd feel terrible living on a passionate island. You'd never know when it was going to go dashing off after another island. Or it might even fall in love with a passing boat. Imagine that.'

'Frightful,' agreed Claudia. She'd been foolish to ask about Evvie's novel, since it was all about love. Not, she thought, that she'd have been able to prevent Evvie from talking about it – asked or unasked.

'All the really torrid titles have been used up time and again. I'll probably end with A Grope in the Heather,' said Evvie. 'Or maybe Island Fling.'

'That would be pretty,' said Claudia.

Evvie looked at her. Claudia seemed quite serious. She really was a bit dim, decided Evvie. 'Are you coming to the vet's party then?' she asked.

'Am I *what*?' said Claudia, pausing in the act of salting the spinach.

'Coming to the Scotch vet's party,' said Evvie patiently. 'I told you about it.'

'No, you didn't,' said Claudia.

'Well, maybe I forgot,' said Evvie, 'but he asked me to bring you. He said to bring my friend in the blue frock. I think he's getting sick of the fiasco. I am too. And Bridie. She keeps bleating. A few pages back I nearly pushed her off a cliff.'

Claudia attempted to unravel fact from fiction. 'I haven't got a blue frock,' she said. 'I told you I haven't.'

Evvie waved her hand impatiently. 'Maybe he got that bit wrong,' she said. 'But he'll be terribly disappointed if I don't bring you.'

'Take Philip,' said Claudia. 'He should be back soon.' She wasn't sure why she said that. It was partly masochism, partly just to speak his name, and partly a spell to bring him back.

'I can't take Philip,' said Evvie. 'The vet doesn't want fairies at his party. He wants to meet *people*. He wants *you* to come.'

'What?' said Claudia after a while. She was standing by the window gazing through it into darkness.

'I said he wants to see *you*,' said Evvie spluttering slightly on a mouthful of spinach.

'Before that,' said Claudia. 'About Philip.'

'I said the vet didn't want to meet faggots,' said Evvie. 'Why?'

'Oh nothing,' said Claudia. 'Nothing at all.'

*

'Claudia's getting dimmer by the minute,' said Evvie to Sylvie when she got home. 'I just mentioned in passing about Philip being queer and she seemed startled. Do you think she didn't know?'

'Evvie, you *didn't*,' said Sylvie.

'Yes I did,' said Evvie, surprised. 'Why not?'

'I never thought,' said Sylvie, 'that I'd need to explain this to you, but it simply is not *comme il faut* to go round telling people that their stepchildren are queer. It simply isn't *done*.'

'Oh Mum,' said Evvie aggrievedly. 'This is 1983.'

'I don't care if it's 1984, said Sylvie. 'You just don't do it.'

'It was all right, Mum. Honestly. She didn't mind. She was acting a bit peculiarly, but then she has been for ages. At one point she just sat down and laughed so much I thought she was going to have a fit. I think it was something I told her about my novel.' Evvie sounded doubtful. 'It wasn't that funny,' she said.

'Was Charles there?' asked Sylvie suddenly.

'No,' said Evvie. 'He was dining in Oxford.'

'Thank God for that,' said Sylvie. 'No matter whether he

knows or he doesn't, don't you ever dare to chatter to him about Philip's sexual inclinations.'

'I hardly ever talk to Charles,' said Evvie.

'I don't care,' said Sylvie. 'I'm beginning to think you capable of anything. I'm beginning to picture you leaping into rooms full of people and announcing that their breath smells, or their wives are running a white-slave trading-post or something. And *you* talk about unstudied utterance. You have the gall to accuse that poor vet of speaking without thinking. Honestly, Evvie!'

'I *was* thinking,' said Evvie. 'I just don't happen to feel that it matters if everyone's queer.'

'That isn't the point. Grrrr,' said Sylvie, clutching her hair. 'Poor Claudia. One minute Gloria's driving her into a ditch, and the next you tell her that.'

'It didn't matter,' insisted Evvie. 'She didn't mind a bit. *And* she's coming to the vet's party. She said she would.'

'Hmmm,' said Sylvie grimly.

*

When Philip came home he was just the same – just as beautiful, calm and affectionate. Claudia blushed when she saw him. He kissed her cheek and regarded her gravely. 'Well?' he said.

'Well,' repeated Claudia, uttering a low, faintly crazy laugh. She left his side and fled to the kitchen wondering what she could find to do there. She supposed she could always peel a few potatoes. She had realised the instant she saw him that nothing had changed, and she loved him.

'It'll be easier now,' she said the kitchen sink. I shall just love him and he shall be my son, she assured herself. Only first I have to learn how to look him in the eye. The apple of my eye. She felt as though she was very slowly bleeding to death. It was, at the moment, painless, but it was debilitating.

*

At dinner Philip and Charles spoke of printing matters, and Claudia was excluded. She understood nothing of the techniques or the concepts, nor the terms they used to describe them. They said not one word which might link their conversation to anything in her own experience. Claudia liked proper words, such as 'bird' and 'crimson', which rallied her imagination and encouraged her intelligence to function. Phrases such as 'cost-effective' and 'computer soft-ware' were to her completely unintelligible and entirely irrelevant. But she didn't say so, because Charles would have been cross with her. He would have asked where she thought the money to keep her in comfort came from: out of the subject of the conversation that was boring her so badly – that's where. Claudia liked talking about people, herself and clothes, and religion sometimes, and love. She thought of the Kentish Town dinner and of how no one had said anything important or structured, or to do with the nature of commercial reality, and how she had enjoyed it. It had been like school when no one had had any sense of responsibility at all, except for a few prefects. Claudia thought Charles was very like a prefect. He had the same propensity to ask sharply what you were giggling about, and to accuse you of slacking and shirking and not pulling your weight and letting the side down. She thought with shame that she was a very trivial woman, a butterfly. A wicked butterfly with unnatural desires. Why, she wondered apathetically, did God bother to make butterflies. They were of no use to anyone. People just collected them or looked at them. No one had a relationship with a butterfly. Her sense of worthlessness was beginning to overwhelm her, and she couldn't call to mind a single useful thing she had ever done. Even her children were away at school being looked after by other people.

'Would you like some pudding?' she asked across a remark about hot metal.

'Good God, no,' said Charles. 'You've already given us enough for half a dozen.'

There you are then, thought Claudia. I don't do anything right. She gathered up the plates, took them into the kitchen and washed them because that needed no real skill and was a sufficiently humble and useful task.

Philip came out after a while and dried them for her. It was very kind, and Claudia liked being alone with him in the warmth of the kitchen; but he did it as deftly as she herself would have done, and what seemed to her odd. She would have preferred it if he had dropped one or two small articles or used the wrong cloth. Not Philip. Everything was put away just where it belonged and the cloth hung neatly to dry on the Aga rail where she herself always put it. It was clear that Philip could fend for himself in matters domestic, and it was disheartening.

18

Sylvie found her in the same mood when she called in the morning. Claudia was surprised to see her – so surprised that for a moment her dreariness fell from her like a covering of ice shattered by a sudden blow.

'It's not all that strange, Claudia,' said Sylvie. 'I do leave the house sometimes.'

'Yes,' said Claudia, 'but you haven't been here for ages. How did you get here anyway?'

'The gamekeeper was going somewhere, so I made him drop me,' explained Sylvie. 'I may smell a bit doggy.'

As Claudia's surprise wore off she began to wilt. 'It was sweet of you to come,' she said, 'but I can't think why you should bother to see me. I'm terrible company at present.'

'Oh, fiddlesticks,' said Sylvie briskly. She had never, actually, found Claudia to be brilliant company, but she was pleasant and nice to look at, and she had no horrible habits. 'I came because I was worried about you. 'You're not yourself.'

'I think I am,' said Claudia mournfully. 'I think I'm completely pointless, and I've only just realised it.'

Now Sylvie found this extremely difficult. She could not deny that there was about Claudia a certain pointlessness, but she had never foreseen that Claudia might become aware of it. There are some friends whose defects are so inherent that it is mere unkindness to hope that they will discover them, and Claudia was certainly one of these.

Sylvie could think of nothing better to say than: 'You're

no more pointless than Gloria.' Even as she uttered this remark she thought it worthy of Evvie or the vet, and wished it unsaid. 'You're very lovable and you don't bite people,' she embellished, as the correct form of words came to her. 'You've got much more point than me,' she said. 'You've got Charles and little children. You're beautiful, and you make your house beautiful, and you look after people. I don't do anything like that.' She wondered why she didn't mind that this was true. She could think of no reason why she should be so content. 'You're much nicer than me,' she added. 'I'm not very nice.'

Claudia did not deny this, and Sylvie gave a snort of astonished amusement as she realised that Claudia was quite aware of *her* friend's defects.

'No, but you're clever,' said Claudia, 'and you're strong and you think about things. I just feel empty.'

She looked empty. She looked bereft, as though some vital organ had been taken from her.

'I have no right to the person I love,' she said, 'and I never knew how much that would hurt. And as far as I'm concerned he might be dead, and I feel as though I was dying. I feel like one of those animals that goes away to die by itself. It must be so terrible not to be a part of life, not to be in the middle of it. So lonely. Oh Sylvie, I'm so lonely.'

Sylvie was beginning to be ashamed of herself. She had forgotten that it doesn't take great intelligence to experience pain. Her assessment of Claudia had been arrogant and thoughtless. Claudia had a hitherto unsuspected capacity for suffering, and if she had been religious Sylvie would have advised her to offer it up. As it was, she could think of no purpose or direction for all that pain and feared that it might fester and stagnate until it poisoned the bearer.

'It's almost worse than if he was dead,' said Claudia flatly.

Sylvie thought about that. In one of the neighbouring

villages lived the widow of a soldier who had recently died committing an act of spectacular bravery. From what Sylvie had gathered there had been no need for his bravery to be quite so spectacular. He could have crouched in a comparatively safe fox-hole and pressed a button – but, no, he had chosen to go, as it were, by the scenic route. For this a grateful Queen and country had awarded him a posthumous medal. Now the widow did not look as Claudia was looking. She wore a calm, almost complacent air, and she had some sons who also wore it. Sylvie knew that, if Queen and country demanded it, they would all, widow and sons alike, agree without a moment's hesitation that those same sons should go in their turn and get their heads blown off. Sylvie had seen the widow a few months before wearing a blue frock with flowers on and she had found her completely terrifying. 'It's a great thing to be able to suffer so,' she said.

'Oh Sylvie,' said Claudia. She laughed, and for an instant she seemed by far the older and the wiser of the two.

Sylvie stayed for lunch and Claudia taught her how to make *beurre blanc*. It was not a skill that Sylvie thought she would often use but she found it quite pleasant and restful to be taught. 'I'd forgotten how nice kitchens could be,' she said, warming her bottom against the Aga. 'I think I miss a lot.'

'You're just trying to be kind to me,' said Claudia, gently moving her along so that she could open the oven. 'It's very sweet of you, but you needn't bother. I expect I'll get over it in time.'

'Truly,' said Sylvie, 'truly I like it here. I can quite see why Evvie comes so often.'

'You don't mind, do you?' asked Claudia.

'No, I don't mind,' said Sylvie. Part of her reason for coming this morning was to try and ascertain whether she should feel it necessary to apologise for Evvie's frank and open ways. 'Do you mind?' she asked.

'Mind?' said Claudia. 'Who? Evvie? No, I don't mind. I'm very fond of her. She makes me laugh.'

'She can be a bit unguarded sometimes in what she says,' offered Sylvie carefully.

Claudia braced herself. 'Just let me get at the oven again a sec,' she said. 'I want to look at the fish.' She knew it would seem unnatural to avoid all mention of Philip – not to agree, cheerfully, that yes, Evvie could be, sometimes, just a touch indiscreet. She straightened up. 'You mustn't worry about what she says. She didn't tell me anything I didn't know.'

'No,' said Sylvie, looking relieved. 'I suppose if you weren't certain before, after your dinner party in London you'd know.' Claudia's account of her dinner party had made her think of Snow White and her Seven Dwarves. Sylvie thought it likely that, in view of Snow White's character, the handsome prince, when he came along, was as queer as a coot too. When princes were as handsome as that they usually were – merely an eighth dwarf. Besides, when princes were roaming the woods on their own they were probably trying to get away from their mother.

'Yes,' said Claudia. 'I don't know what Charles thinks. I wouldn't like Evvie to talk to him about it. We've never discussed it.'

'I've told her that,' said Sylvie. 'I've indicated to her that if she utters one squeak to Charles her life expectancy will be rather less than she'd thought.'

'I don't even know if he'd care,' said Claudia. 'I sometimes wonder if Charles cares about anything apart from his beastly press. Perhaps if he'd taken more notice of Philip, Philip wouldn't be – like this.'

'That's not fair,' protested Sylvie. 'Philip's mother grabbed him. You know she did. Charles didn't stand a chance.'

'Oh, I know,' said Claudia. 'I just get so cross with Charles sometimes. I know he has to work hard, but he's got so crusty. He isn't any fun.'

Sylvie thought – well, of course he isn't any fun. Nobody's any fun when their wife's breaking her heart over someone else. She said: 'I think he does care, you know. I know Charles well enough to know he'd care.'

'About Philip?' asked Claudia.

'I don't know about Philip,' said Sylvie. 'I just think he'd mind about you.'

'He doesn't seem to,' said Claudia.

Of course he doesn't seem to, thought Sylvie. He's terrified of precipitating something. You are a silly woman, Claudia. She wished she could say so aloud, but it was much too late to announce that she'd been elected Charles's confidante. 'Completely heterosexual men take a tragic attitude to the world,' she said. 'They take things terribly seriously because they feel the awful responsibility of looking after their families. And then they have that terrible urge to make war all the time, and that can't be too good for their digestions.'

'Well, I prefer the other sort,' said Claudia, suddenly childish. 'At least they make me laugh.' Which was a foolish remark in view of the tears that Philip had cost her. 'I don't know why you're defending men,' she said. 'You got rid of yours soon enough.'

'Jack was barking mad,' said Sylvie. 'He was so aggressive his emotions were muscle-bound. He was so male he could only relate to other males. God knows what that made him.'

'I quite liked him in the end,' said Claudia. 'I never told you before, but when you were divorcing him he used to come and talk to me about it. I was awfully sorry for him.'

*

'Can you *beat* it?' asked Sylvie of Gloria when Claudia had run her home. 'Can you just beat it? Did you ever hear anything so ridiculous in all your dog's days?'

116

Gloria laid her jaw along Sylvie's knee and gazed up at her trustingly.

'It is funny,' said Sylvie. 'You've got to admit it's funny. Even you, dog, who have little sense of humour, you have to admit it's funny.'

Gloria raised and lowered her tail to the floor – twice.

*

'Mum,' said Evvie, 'do you think I could bear to write "His bosom heaved with suppressed manly emotion"?'

'Well, *I* couldn't,' said Sylvie, 'but I daresay *you* could.'

'Fungus has just had his baby, see. At least, I mean, Amaryllis has, and he's all of a twitter.'

'Congratulations,' said Sylvie idly.

Evvie pondered briefly and wrote: 'Fergus and Clara gazed at each other, moist-eyed, united for a brief moment by wonder at the ever-fresh miracle of birth. "Thank ye, dear Clara," muttered Fergus huskily. "I s'all ne'er forget this." "Whaddaya mean *you'll* never forget it," screamed Amaryllis. "Whaddaya know about it, you damn two-timing, frog-faced son of a bitch – you *man*, you." ' Evvie crossed out that last bit and wrote: ' "Amaryllis," murmured Fergus tenderly, "we ha'e a dear wee dochter." Amaryllis tossed her head petulantly. "I don't want to see it," she moaned. "I don't like it. Take it away." A shadow briefly clouded Fergus's noble features, but he took the tiny creature and handed it to Clara, who stood waiting patiently at the foot of the rumpled bed in the fitful lamplight. "Rest noo ma dearest," Fergus murmured lovingly to Amaryllis. "Piss off," said Amaryllis, heaving the bed pan at his head.'

'You spend more time crossing things out than you do writing them,' said Sylvie, observing her daughter.

'I keep getting carried away,' said Evvie. She wrote:

'Fergus picked up the calving chains and left the chamber.' She giggled.

'At least it amuses you,' said her mother.

Evvie frowned. 'That's the trouble,' she said. 'There's a £40,000 prize on offer for a Romance and I'm determined to get it, but if I can't keep a straight face I don't stand a chance.' She bent over her paper and started to write again. 'I think I'll make Amaryllis a writer too,' she said after a while, 'and I'll quote lots of her prose which will be absolutely marvellous, and she can make it clear to the reader how *painful* it is to be an author.'

'You've left it a bit late, haven't you?' said Sylvie. 'I thought you were romping up to the *dénouement*.'

'I'll have to go back and put bits in,' said Evvie. 'Every ten pages or so I'll get old Amaryllis to dash off a few lines of deathless verse.'

'She doesn't sound to me like a deathless verse girl,' objected Sylvie. 'If she wrote at all, which I doubt, she'd be the absolutely worst sort of gossip columnist.'

'Oh, all right,' said Evvie. 'I'll do that next time. Do you suppose Amaryllis plays the violin?'

'No,' said Sylvie, 'not for a moment do I suppose that Amaryllis plays the violin.'

'I guess you're right,' said Evvie. 'But they're all a bit lacking in culture. They hardly do anything but get pregnant and try and push each other out of boats. Maybe the Laird tinkles the odd tune on the grand piano.'

'Then you've got the same problem,' said Sylvie. 'You'll have to go back to the beginning and insert bits. You can hardly have him taking up music on the last page.'

'They'll all just have to get on with it.' Evvie sighed. 'I feel sorry for them. They must be bored out of their heads on that diabolical island. Still, I expect they'll enjoy being famous. I'm sure they'd put up with any amount of discomfort just to see themselves in print.'

Sylvie felt a touch dizzy 'Evvie,' she said. 'They're not *real*.'

'They are, sort of,' said Evvie. 'They're real to me. I think I'll take Bridie for a walk. I've got a feeling I've left her sitting in the kitchen for about six months now.'

*

When Evvie got back to her room she thumbed idly through her Horace. Were *his* characters real, she wondered – his Chloë, Phyllis, Lalage, Pyrrha, Cinara and the rest? Not to mention the pretty boys, Ligurinus and Lyciscus. Evvie turned up the commentators to find some answers. Unfortunately she found too many: the grammarians wrangled, rushing round in their mini-chariots raising an Olympic dust. According to his biographer, Horace's room had been lined with mirrors so that he could observe love from every angle, and certainly what Evvie liked about him was this endless interest in people's antics. Horace would have made an excellent novelist, she thought.

19

Claudia, looking around at her immaculate house, decided that the time had come for an autumn clean. Her sense of guilt and inadequacy had beaten her into a servile mood. Like Gloria, after one of her more deplorable lapses, she felt the need to creep along the ground and lick boots. It was not so much her forbidden love that had brought her to this pass as her defiance of Charles. She felt that she had been behaving with outrageous foolhardiness, like a puny cabin boy who has cheeked the head buccaneer in the midst of the mighty ocean. Now she must make amends or take the consequences. She no longer snapped at Charles or told him to wait for his tea, but deferred to his every opinion and trembled at his irritation. She had recognised again his enormous power, and realised that to flout it would be to invite, not only her own destruction, but the destruction of all the world about her. Wistfully, she sometimes thought of Kentish Town and those gentle creatures in whose company she had felt so at ease, since they had made no demands upon her. She found she now agreed with Sylvie that somewhere in the relations between the sexes there lay a huge murderousness, and she sneaked around her life on stockinged feet, determined to give no offence.

Charles was relieved to find her normal again.

'Edith,' said Claudia. 'I want to do out all the cupboards and wash the china. It's pouring with rain, I can't go out, so we'll do it today.'

Edith thought this a waste of time since the china was perfectly clean and most of it was never used anyway, but she knew Claudia's funny ideas, and she was well paid. 'You going to do it, or me?' she enquired. Claudia had explained years ago that she would herself wash the precious things. Then, if they broke, only she could be blamed.

'You can pass them to me and I'll wash them,' said Claudia, who, as a penance, was going to spend the morning working beside Edith. It was her place, she thought, endlessly to slave at the eternal task of keeping things clean. She would have scrubbed the floor on her hands and knees in her urge to escape retribution, but Edith would have thought she'd gone mad – as, in a way, she had.

*

Late in the morning God was good to her. He sent Philip home with a sore throat. Claudia's anxiety dissipated, her panic melted away. Ill people presented a definite, clear-cut purpose. They had to be looked after. Illness was an essential component of society, forcing those still on their feet to display qualities of compassion and concern which would otherwise never become apparent. Infants perform much the same function. Claudia had never experienced those feelings of panicked purposelessness with a baby at her breast but had regarded everyone with love. It made little difference to her that it was Philip who stood in need of succour. Had a bleeding beggar crawled to her threshold she would have been just as content.

'First you must have a hot bath,' she told Philip. 'I'll get you a warm towel from the airing cupboard. Then I'll bring you some hot lemon and an aspirin, and I'll make some cold lemon for you to sip.'

Philip did say that he'd rather sit in the drawing-room, and he didn't feel all that ill, and had only come home because Charles didn't want him spreading infection, but Claudia didn't listen. She wasn't letting him off so easily.

When he was in bed she put her hand on his forehead and he put his hand over hers. The very slightness of this gesture made it seem more explicitly erotic than if he'd pinched her bottom, so Claudia reminded herself that Philip would necessarily find the female form repulsive and hastened away. Her hands shook as she filled a hot-water bottle. 'Edith,' she said, 'take this up to Philip, will you. I must get this china done before lunch time.'

After lunch she went through the pantry, throwing away the few ounces of beans and lentils and raisins that seemed always to be left imprisoned in large jars, as though she had intended to be provident, keeping them for a rainy day, but now that a rainy day had come she was throwing them out. Much of life was quite pointless, decided Claudia, but she found she didn't care.

By the time dusk fell she was completely relaxed. The house smelled as clean as water, and upstairs she had an ailing human being to be cossetted. As soon as Edith had gone she put thin bread and butter and a cup of china tea on a tray and took them upstairs. Often at tea time she was assailed by feelings of sorrow and loss. If it was summer, and the children not yet home for the holidays, she would feel her throat swell at the memory of banana sandwiches and strawberries, and in the winter the smell of warm buttered toast almost made her cry. She had never spoken to anyone of this babyish trait, though sometimes she had wondered whether it was her own childhood that she mourned, or the childhood of her children.

This evening she felt no sorrow. She felt whole, as though her child, her lover and her self had assumed one form and sat with her in the dusk, taking tea and bread and butter.

*

Philip came downstairs at supper time wearing a black

122

dressing gown. He knelt by the fire in the drawing room with an air of oriental remoteness and calm. Claudia could have sat and watched him till the end of time, but then Charles came home. He came into the room still in his dark blue overcoat, brown trilby and brown shoes, and he looked so different from Philip that they might have belonged to different species.

Claudia's mood had changed again. Now that her anxiety had left her she had lost her fear of Charles's displeasure, and she regarded him critically. He looked primitive beside Philip; unevolved, like Cro Magnon man. Claudia, unknown to herself, was beginning to take the view that the higher civilisations are distinguished by a certain similarity between the sexes, an androgynous blurring of the definitions. Had she been in the way of examining her reactions and translating them into thought, she would eventually have arrived at the word 'decadent', though still nothing would have persuaded her to apply it to Philip.

She sat thinking dreamily that Philip was like a flower while Charles resembled a round of beef, and then was shocked by the realisation that in one short day she had gone off her husband again. One minute she was yearning for his approval and protection and the next she was despising him. She was growing weary of the kaleidoscopic state of her emotions and counted days to see if she could be suffering from pre-menstrual tension.

'What's that thing you're wearing?' Charles demanded of Philip.

'It's a kimono,' said Claudia.

'Thought for a minute he'd got one of your frocks on,' said Charles without much interest. He was another of those who habitually spoke his mind.

'Oh Charles,' said Claudia, 'not everyone wears those hairy old khaki dressing gowns.'

'Well, they should,' said Charles, going off to remove his hat and coat.

Claudia burned with temper.

Then when Charles came back he said plaintively, 'I'm tired.'

He lay on the sofa, and he *looked* tired, so Claudia's mood changed again. 'Oh, poor Charles,' she said, 'shall I take your shoes off for you?'

Charles, eyes closed, said in even, unthinking tones: 'Don't be bloody silly. I'm not a baby.' So Claudia's mood changed yet again.

'If you're that tired,' she remarked in fish-wifely fashion, 'you won't want your dinner. I'll just give Philip his.'

'I'll have it later,' said Charles. 'I'm going to have a little snooze first.'

'I'll wait too,' said Philip. 'We can have it together later.' And at that Claudia could have murdered the pair of them. She went off to bed in the studio and lay staring at the ceiling.

*

At midnight the door opened.

'Claudia,' said Philip's voice.

She sat up.

'I just wondered if you were all right,' said the voice.

Now that she could see the speaker, aureoled in the light from the landing she saw that it was Charles. For the first time she realised that he and Philip had the same voice.

'I was asleep,' she said. 'I've been asleep for a long time.'

*

Claudia lay awake all night, thinking. She thought that as Charles had grown older, more mature, more worried, more male, he had left her behind. She thought that she too had tried to grow up in her own way, but as Charles refused to see the relevance of her experience he thought her infantile. She thought that Charles could scarcely

124

differentiate between women and children. The result, concluded Claudia, was that she now saw Charles as a father. And the result of that, she said to the darkness, was that it seemed to her that it would be rather more incestuous to sleep with Charles than with his son.

*

Came the dawn. Claudia lay and watched the light returning. So Philip was his father's son; she saw his father as her own father. Where did that leave them? It was wearily confusing. She was beginning to think that Sylvie's ruthless severing of all human connections was the only rational response to this stew of affinities. In the cold grey morning Claudia accepted that unless she got some fell disease, or was caused by Gloria to die on the roads, she had years and years to live, and was already very tired.

She decided, with renewed panic, that she was one of those luckless creatures trapped in a loveless marriage and leapt out of bed determined to do something about it. She would put aside her dream of love and damn well get on with her husband. In the end, he was all she had.

She went downstairs and made a pot of tea. She went upstairs again and shook Charles gently by the shoulder. 'I brought you a cup of tea,' she said.

Charles woke and turned, staring at her without recognition like a wild animal. 'What the hell are you doing?' he said. 'I hardly slept at all last night and now you've woken me up.' He flung himself over on to his other side, spilling the tea. It stained the edge of the sheets, and probably the mattress too.

Claudia took the cup downstairs again and washed it.

*

It was the same over the next few days. At one minute Charles would say something annoying and Claudia would respond with rage. Then she would grow anxious and creep to him for reassurance, only to be met with indifference. If things had gone well at the works Charles would be in an expansive and affectionate frame of mind, and Claudia would fail to respond at all. They were like a piece of machinery into which someone has thrown a spanner, all the moving parts grinding away, hopelessly at odds with each other.

Claudia tried to explain something of this to Sylvie.

'You know what I always say,' said Sylvie. 'I say men and women are incompatible and shouldn't spend much time together at all. We're not like birds. Swans and pigeons and things seems to muddle along quite happily, but most mammals don't. They get together for a swift spot of the other, then they go their separate ways. You don't find them sitting opposite each other in the evenings by the fire. Remember hamsters. Put a male and a female in a cage, and they end by eating each other up. Think of the corpses we buried when the kiddos were in the pet stage.'

'That can't be true,' said Claudia. 'I couldn't bear to live alone. There are hundreds of perfectly happily married people.'

'I don't know any,' said Sylvie.

'*I* do,' insisted Claudia. 'It's just that you think they're boring, so you don't want to know them.'

'If there are,' said Sylvie, 'this is how they do it. Either they have secret lovers which puts them in such a good temper they're nice to everyone, or they don't talk to each other. Then each can assume that the other is thinking the same as himself, or herself, as the case may be. People always assume that other people are the same as themselves until they open their mouths and prove it not to be so.'

It was what she'd said to Charles. He hadn't believed her and Sylvie didn't imagine that Claudia would. She didn't know why she was wasting her breath.

'That's a very cynical view,' protested Claudia, 'and it's unchristian.'

'No it isn't,' said Sylvie. 'Christ had no time for marriage. Marriage is a completely secular notion. It began simply as a means of ensuring that property stayed in the right genetic hands. Then that looked a bit dirty, so they dressed it up with a lot of sacramental stuff.'

'I think that's heresy,' said Claudia.

'I think you're right,' said Sylvie tranquilly, 'but it's true all the same.'

*

When they had finished this conversation, Claudia sat by her telephone thinking that Sylvie would probably not be in the least shocked to learn that she was in love with Philip. And Sylvie sat by hers wishing that she hadn't said that thing about lovers, because Claudia was far from being the sort of person who could happily deceive her husband.

20

The night before Hallowe'en Evvie drove home early. It was growing colder and Evvie felt as though she was speeding into winter. She was glad to see smoke rising from the cottage chimney. Sometimes her mother forgot to light the fire and never seemed to realise that she was cold herself.

'I've nearly finished my book,' announced Evvie, removing her crash helmet and turning her face from Gloria, who had risen, had put her legs round her neck and was licking her.

'Gloria,' said Sylvie warningly.

Gloria had swiftly bitten the gamekeeper's brother a few days before, out of a clear blue sky. Sylvie did not like to think her treacherous, preferring to believe that sometimes Gloria was simply overwhelmed by the desire to sink her teeth in human flesh; nevertheless there was something distinctly Judas-like in her present behaviour. Reluctantly, Gloria dropped back on all-fours looking sullen and thwarted.

Sylvie put another log on the fire. 'These come from the rotten beams that they took out of the roof,' she said. 'It feels funny giving the cottage bits of itself to eat. Like a final form of cannibalism.'

'On Monday,' said Evvie, 'I'm sending my novel off to be typed. Then I'm sending it straight to Philip's mother.'

'And what about Roman poetry?' asked Sylvie.

'That's all taken care of,' said Evvie. 'I'm going to get a Double First. You know quite well I am.'

'It's good to have confidence,' said Sylvie, 'but sometimes I think yours may be just the teeniest touch extreme.'

'I'm not *over*confident. Truly,' said Evvie. 'I've got strong doubts about bits of my book. The bedroom bits mostly. There never used to be any sex in romantic novels. There is now, but you mustn't overdo it, or all the romance disappears. The readership wants just a hint of something naughty.'

'In early films,' said Sylvie, 'they got round all that by insisting on twin beds, and if anything risky was going on the heroine had to have one foot on the floor.'

'I don't think they have twin beds in crofters' cabins,' said Evvie. 'I don't think they have beds at all. I think they sleep on fertiliser sacks, so that'd mean *all* of her would be on the floor – which rather defeats the object of the exercise. I can't count how many bedroom doors I've discreetly closed.'

'Much the best way,' said Sylvie comfortably. 'All that heaving and panting and swinging from the chandelier is very taxing on the average reader. Have you thought of a title yet?'

'I thought I might call it Till a' the Seas Gang Dry,' said Evvie. 'Only I'm not sure who it'd apply to. They're not a very faithful lot, my lot.'

'Sentiments of eternal fidelity are rather surprising coming from the poet Burns,' said Sylvie, 'but it's a pretty conceit.'

'Burns was rather like Horace really,' said Evvie. 'He wasn't a Romantic. Unconscious artistry, the illusion of spontaneity, perfect rendering of the eternal platitudes – that's what both of them were after. Just like me really. Besides, they were both of low degree yet perfect gentlemen. Unlike the Scotch vet.' She scowled. 'Do you think Fungus might luve – I mean – love Amaryllis till the rocks melt wi' the sun?'

'I suppose he might,' said Sylvie. 'But if he's got any sense he'll settle for Clara. At least she can cook.'

'Cooking doesn't matter in the romantic novel,' said Evvie. 'It's only mentioned so that the goofy girl – the good, gentle one with the soft curls – can appear with a smudge of flour on her stupid nose.'

'Maybe you could let them all wither away from starvation,' suggested Sylvie. 'That'd be different.'

'Don't forget the mackerel,' said Evvie. 'I get the impression that the mackerel more or less leap out of the sea and force themselves down their throats.'

'I'm looking forward to reading the finished version,' said Sylvie. 'I'll be interested to see how you tie it all up.'

'I'd better go and do that now,' said Evvie. 'I've given myself a Sunday deadline and I need two thousand words.'

*

'The sun was setting o'er the silver sea ... ' Like a jelly on a plate, thought Evvie. Oh, blast. 'A peaceful calm lay o'er the silent island.' Now why was that, wondered Evvie. Had they all finally killed each other? She waited to see who was going to appear on the brow of the hill. It was Clara, carrying something. 'Clara stumbled painfully along the rock-strewn path, blinded by bitter tears. No longer could she bear her husband's cruelty, his taunts, his evil ways ...' Right, thought Evvie, so she's nipped away with all her belongings in a red spotted hankie. Now where's she going? 'Clara stumbled, weeping, up to the weather-beaten door of Fergus's house, and half fell, half knocked upon it. Bridie opened it. "Och weel, come awa' in," she remarked ...' No, hang on. That wouldn't do. Amaryllis wouldn't stand for having Clara on the premises. Evvie thought hard until inspiration came to her. Amaryllis had gone away, and Evvie knew where. She'd taken the wolfhound and whipped off to London to start a literary agency, vowing never to return until they'd cleaned the place up a bit – got new curtains, put in electricity and mains water, and washed the paintwork. 'Safe at last in the haven of Fergus's absolutely ghastly sitting room … ' No. ' … in the haven of Fergus's manly arms, Clara felt her heart swell with happiness.' There was something wrong. Something missing. Oh help, Clara had forgotten the baby. She'd had it about a month ago, and she'd left it to the tender mercies of the Laird. Hastily Evvie put Clara back on the brow of the hill, carrying a small, white-wrapped bundle this time. ' "We sha' bring the wee bairns up taegither," murmured Fergus brokenly … ' Because naturally Amaryllis hadn't bothered to take hers. Nappies and bassinettes were not Amaryllis's style at all. Evvie took a brief tally of her characters. Bridie was in the kitchen burning bannocks and going och, weel in a contented fashion. The Laird was chewing his whiskers, and biting the rug in foiled rage back in the castle. Mango and the fisher-lass were probably still at it down by the sea shore. Amaryllis was whooping it up in London … Right. Evvie took her pen. 'Clara lifted her winsome face to Fergus. At last their lips met in a long, lingering kiss. The seal of their eternal love.' '*Ugh*,' said Evvie with acute distaste. ' "Och, ma wee luve," breathed Fergus. "Noo I ha'e ye in ma arms I'm going to … " ' 'Oh no you're not,' said Evvie. 'Not in *my* book you're not.' Firmly she wrote. ' "Noo I ha'e ye i' ma arms I s'all ne'er le' ye goo".' She wondered whether, north of the border, they left the consonants out of words like 'arms', then decided that they couldn't. Not even them.

'Well, that's that, Mum,' said Evvie, coming downstairs with an air of achievement. 'Some of it was jolly difficult. I'm never going to do dialect again. For some reason, every now and then they started talking Deep South instead of Scotch, saying 'agwine' and 'waal' and drawling. Jolly irritating.'

In the middle of supper Evvie paused in the act of eating

a mouthful of baked beans. She gazed into the middle distance with an expression of total dismay.

'What's wrong?' asked her mother, following the direction of her gaze.

'Oh God,' said Evvie, 'do you know what I've done?'

'What have you done?' said Sylvie, beginning to worry. 'Come on, what is it?'

'I've only left Violet on the other side of the island, tethered to a stump. She must've eaten all the grass pages ago. She'll be going *mad*.' Evvie got up from the table. 'I'll have to bring her back. I can't think what to do with her. She won't have Clara round, and I can't send her to London with Amaryllis.'

'Chop her up, for goodness sake, and stick her in the deep freeze,' said Sylvie crossly. 'You gave me a fright. Do sit down and finish your supper.'

'I can't do that,' said Evvie. 'I'm fond of her. Maybe the vet gives her barbiturates, like Gloria.'

'I didn't want to give Gloria barbiturates,' said Sylvie, 'But I'm afraid I'll have to. She's getting impossible.'

'Violet's been impossible for ages,' said Evvie competitively. 'Maybe she'll be better when she has Fungus's calf.'

'Yes, maybe she will,' said Sylvie. 'Now do eat your supper.'

*

Claudia had no intention of gracing the vet's Hallowe'en party with her presence. It was not only that she didn't want Evvie to realise that she had never actually spoken to the Scotch vet and so couldn't be having an affair with him, although that might be mildly awkward, but that she felt quite certain that she wouldn't enjoy it. No one she knew would be there, and Claudia was still shy among strangers.

Evvie drove up at mid morning to make sure that she

132

was coming. 'You *promised*,' she grizzled. 'You *said* you would.'

'I didn't promise,' said Claudia. 'I never actually said I would. Not once.'

'You didn't say you wouldn't,' said Evvie. 'I was sure you'd come. You are mean. It won't be any fun by myself.'

'Don't go,' suggested Claudia. 'If you've finished your book you don't need to go.'

'But I *do*,' said Evvie. 'I want just a final look round to see if there's anything I really should add. It's *necessary* for me to go.'

'Make Sylvie go with you,' said Claudia.

'Mum doesn't drive,' said Evvie revealingly.

'Oh, I see,' said Claudia. 'I'll take you, if you like, and I'll come and bring you back, but I won't stay.'

'It isn't just your car I want,' said Evvie. 'I want *you* to come.'

Philip who had been wandering in and out of the kitchen in his grave, quiet way suddenly said: 'You *must* go. Think what fun it will be – a bonfire and people in masks, and pumpkin lanterns.'

'You're not persuading me,' said Claudia.

'Apple bobbing,' went on Philip, 'parkin and treacle toffee. Perhaps they'll roast a pig on a spit.'

'You're making it sound worse,' said Claudia.

'Hot punch with roasted crab apples, people on broomsticks ... '

Claudia began to laugh. 'Charles,' she said, as he came in for his coffee. 'Do you think I should go to the vet's party?'

'No, of course not,' said Charles. 'Bloody silly idea.'

'All right,' said Claudia. 'I'll go if you will too, Philip.'

*

'I promised Claudia I'd make sure Violet was locked in her field, so then she said she'd come,' concluded Evvie.

'You shouldn't bully people like that,' said Sylvie. 'It's very ill-mannered.'

'It wasn't me,' said Evvie. 'I was just about to give up Then Philip persuaded her At least I think it was Philip. She just suddenly gave in.'

'Poor Claudia,' said Sylvie. 'She'll hate it. She hates outdoor things and romps.'

'She can sneak away and cuddle the vet,' said Evvie. 'Get to know him better.'

'Evvie,' said Sylvie. 'If I hear that you've said anything like that to either of them I will kill you. Truly. I shall have you put down.'

'Oh Mum,' said Evvie. 'Of course I won't. As if I would.'

'Oh you *would*,' said Sylvie. 'I'm just warning you that if you *do* ...'

'Oh hush, Mum,' said Evvie. 'I shall be discretion itself.'

'Huh,' said Sylvie.

'I didn't tell her it's fancy dress,' said Evvie. 'I thought that would put her utterly off. We're supposed to go as witches and warlocks. Can I borrow your old black frock?'

'That old black frock is my only decent dress,' said Sylvie.

'Oh Mum,' said Evvie pleadingly.

'Oh, all right – only don't burn holes in it, or tear it, or use it to mop up the gravy.'

'Of course I won't,' said Evvie, but Sylvie didn't really believe her old black frock would ever be the same again after its Hallowe'en outing.

*

'You look very nice,' said Claudia in surprise when Evvie had arrived and taken off her crash helmet.

'It's my fancy dress,' said Evvie. Claudia thought that Evvie's fancy dress was much more like the ordinary attire of other people than her everyday apparel, but she said reprovingly: 'You didn't say it was fancy dress.'

'I didn't want to frighten you,' said Evvie. 'Anyway I think it'll be quite sufficient if we all wear unrelieved black like a funeral procession.'

Claudia was wearing a plum-coloured velvet coat and skirt. 'Do you mean I've got to change?' she asked, dismayed.

'It won't take you a second,' said Evvie. 'Just slip into something gloomy.'

The only black garment Claudia possessed was the one she had bought in Harrods. There seemed to be no good reason why she shouldn't wear it.

Philip was already clad in black trousers and sweater. 'Can I go on your bike?' he asked Evvie.

'Oh Philip,' cried Claudia, who never worried when Evvie was riding it.

'OK,' said Evvie reluctantly. 'As long as you don't bust it. You'll have to take my crash helmet.'

By the time they were ready to go Claudia looked like the queen of one of the more undesirable fairy-tale kingdoms. Her face was pale, and she had tied her hair back with a black velvet ribbon.

Philip had gone upstairs and come down again wearing a black leather jacket with many zips which Claudia had never seen before.

'What a horrible thing,' she said. To her unaccustomed eyes he resembled a Hell's Angel. When he strapped on the crash helmet she felt that if she met him in the street she would fail to recognise him.

'We do look sinister,' said Evvie with satisfaction.

They made an odd group, all in black. Like misplaced jigsaw pieces of night.

Charles glared at them from the door. 'I wish you'd go if you're going,' he said, 'chattering away like a lot of blasted jackdaws.'

*

'You'll have to introduce Philip to the vet,' said Evvie as Claudia drove out of the gate. 'I can't remember his name. It's MacHaggis or something. I can never remember foreign names. If they're called Macpherson I can never see why they shouldn't just as soon be called Macdonald instead.'

Claudia didn't reply. She was planning to bluff her way through the introductory awkwardness with little laughs and gestures. 'Have you thought of a title for your novel yet?' she asked again.

Evvie was easily diverted. 'I thought of a Love in a Mist,' she said, 'because there's constant fog on the island. It amazes me that they ever found each other for long enough to conceive all those babies. Stumbling round with their hands outstretched. It's like a sort of allegory of human relationships.'

'You talk like your mother,' said Claudia. 'She says people can never know each other and only make it worse if they try.' She sounded sad, as though she hoped Evvie would deny it.

'She's so *right*,' said Evvie enthusiastically. 'There's this girl at my College and her mum made them all go along for something called Family Therapy. Well, it was fine while they were sitting with this benevolent old party who was running the thing – they accused each other of incest and rapine and theft and murder, and he very calmly asked each one of them what they thought about that then, and they all thought about it and spoke in low, thoughtful tones and agreed, yes, the others had a point of view, and they might, themselves, have been a touch selfish. Then when they got into the corridor they started muttering – what did you want to say *that* for, sort of thing – and pushing each other a bit. Then in the vestibule they started screeching, and by the time they got into the street they were rolling round on the pavement and the police had to be called.'

Claudia examined this jaundiced view of the latest techniques in psychotherapy. She had to admit, if she was honest, that the results described by Evvie did not seem to be wholly unlikely.

Someone roared past on a motor bike and she rubbed the windscreen with her knuckles, leaning forward as though to get a closer look. The little red light and the sound had disappeared into the future. 'I wish you hadn't let Philip take your bike,' said Claudia.

'That wasn't Philip,' said Evvie. 'My bike's half that size. Anyway Philip's used to motor bikes. He was *wild* at Oxford. They still speak of him in the SCR in hushed tones.'

'*Philip*?' asked Claudia, turning her head to stare at her.

'Yeah,' said Evvie, staring back. 'Didn't you know?'

There was silence after that, except for the occasional rush of an overtaking car, as Claudia looked back to the time when Philip must have been an undergraduate. The children were tiny then and she had been engrossed in them. She was only now beginning to realise how engrossed. Distant wars and calamities, local quarrels and tragedies had all passed over her head. As this Claudia looked back on that Claudia she found her, in retrospect, almost as wearisome as Sylvie had found her at the time. She had thought of nothing but the babies, nothing but their diets; squashing up endless mixtures of protein and vitamins and roughage, weighing and measuring and counting drops of nutritional supplements. She had spent hours playing educational games with them and wheeling them round in the fresh air, hours reading them stories about rabbits and washing their dear little pinnies. And for what? They would never live with her again for long. They would go off to public schools, then university, then into careers. She would see them briefly in the holidays when they weren't on school trips. Oh, what a goddamn waste of time, thought this Claudia.

It was incomprehensible to her that, if Philip had been as wild as Evvie said he had been, it had never come to her attention. Surely Charles must have been worried and spoken to her about it. She could remember nothing except endless days of mindless happiness. Poor Charles, she thought. I must have bored him to death.

She remembered, with an effort, the times Philip had come to see them, usually with friends. She must have wrenched herself away from the children for long enough to see that they were fed, but they had left no mark on her consciousness. By that time she had lost her fear of Charles's first child. There had been little reason for anything to disturb her content. Oh smug, thought Claudia. Smug, smug, smug …

Evvie was silent because she was sulking. It was clear that she had put her foot in her mouth again, and it wasn't fair. People as stupid as Claudia shouldn't be allowed. They were a danger to the thinking person. If every time an intelligent person made a remark she offended the susceptibilities of an unintelligent person, then there was no point in talking at all. Certainly not if the intelligent person was going to get told off for it. Evvie felt sorry for people like Galileo: it was sickening to have all your accurate observations dismissed with contumely and wrath. She wished she could ask Claudia not to mention to Sylvie that she had once more stated the obvious, but her pride wouldn't permit her.

Bloody hell, thought Evvie, as they approached the vet's house.

21

Sylvie stood in her garden with the dead. Their spirits thronged the upper air. They didn't seem to mind being dead. Sylvie had an impression of serenity and distant appraisal, as though the dead were on a leisurely coach trip through the courses of their past, and not one of them wished to speak to the driver to ask to be let off. They made her feel insignificant – just a figure in a landscape, standing, hand shading her eyes, watching the watchers, the real people, go swiftly by.

Gloria, on the other hand, was twitchy. The hair on her neck bristled and she would suddenly snarl, turning her head in the direction of something unseen, as though an intangible imp had insulted her. She reminded her mistress of a mad person tormented by libidinous phantoms.

'It's your conscience,' said Sylvie. 'You've got a bad conscience.'

Gloria momentarily relaxed at the sound of her beloved's voice. She crept humbly to Sylvie's side, forgetting the adversaries who taunted her in cowardly fashion, taking advantage of their invisibility.

Sylvie could see lights away over the fields, the size of candle flames. The pervasive wood smoke smelled of incense, and night was a black chasuble, sewn with the stars and the moon, with all the far universes hidden in its folds.

She was not surprised to see Charles. She was filled with

disappointment at the loss of her perfect evening, but she knew the rules. Only the dead were permitted complete possession of the evening. The living had to put up with each other.

'Didn't like to think of you all on your own,' said Charles after the initial duel with Gloria.

'That was very kind of you,' said Sylvie.

Charles looked awkward. It had been a fairly dopey remark considering that Sylvie spent all her time on her own. 'I mean, not tonight,' he amended. 'Not with everyone gallivanting off to parties. Thought we could have our own party.'

He had brought a bottle of gin, so that was something. After a couple of stiff ones Sylvie minded him less. He looked unhappy. The flesh of his face had the dough-like consistency that seemed always to characterise masculine unhappiness. Unhappiness was a feminine trait. When men wore it they were unmanned, as though they had donned silk knickers and suspender belt. Perhaps that was why the whole of society was weighted in favour of keeping men happy.

Certainly women were better suited to coping with infidelity and misery. They were used to it, and they had each other. Sylvie thought Charles would pass out on the spot if he knew how women talked to each other. The brutal coarseness of barrack-room boasting paled to infinity beside the detailed indelicacy of the talk of women discussing men who have displeased them.

Charles wanted to know where Claudia had gone. Not the present Claudia – she'd gone to the vet's party. He knew that. He didn't like it, but it worried him less than the loss of the old Claudia – warm, loving Claudia, who never answered back.

'Perhaps she's growing up,' suggested Sylvie, unkindly.

Charles dismissed this with silence and a stern look. Sylvie knew it was hopeless. Men loved a certain Woman. She was tender, complaisant, amorous, beautiful and

140

dumb. Oh goodness, was she dumb. She appeared on the centrefold of magazines, in the pages of the worse male novelists. She was there to be used and abused and she came up smiling every time. Silly bitch.

Sylvie, in the interests of justice, considered her male equivalent who appeared in the pages of the worse women novelists: tall, dark and handsome, manly and brave – not necessarily rich and successful, as men would imagine him to be. Sometimes he was like a little boy in the hands of the female fantasist. Sometimes he was arrogant and overbearing – not the sort you'd ask to dinner. In the end, thought Sylvie, if they ever got together – these two fabulous beasts of sexual imagining – they would serve each other right.

Gloria was still growling under her breath and occasionally lifting her lip.

'That dog is very disturbed,' said Charles.

'I know,' said Sylvie. 'I think she's on heat.' But she wondered if Gloria's dead had returned, and the spirits of past dogs were jeering at her from the shadows.

22

'Ghosties and ghoulies and lang-legged beasties,' said
Evvie glumly, as they went up the drive to the vet's house.
A large bonfire glimmered and swayed before them and
there seemed to be a great many people.

'I thought you said he didn't know anyone,' said
Claudia, switching off the ignition and surveying the scene,
bewildering with chiaroscuro, flame and smoke.

'I said he doesn't know anyone we know,' corrected
Evvie. 'He doesn't either. You'll see.'

Most of the guests seemed to be masked, so Claudia
thought it might be quite difficult to tell.

'I'll go and find Fango and Mungus ... ' began Evvie. Oh
blast. 'That's Violent ... ' she said, waving her hand
proprietorially towards the bottom of the field where
nothing was visible save a tumble of shadow. Conceivably
a cow was included in its composition, but it was not
apparent. Evvie wondered how she could possibly be drunk
when she'd had nothing to drink.

There was very loud music emanating from the house. It
seemed to mingle with the smoke and the shifting light and
combine to dull and pervert the senses. Claudia did not
think she'd be able to stand it for long. She looked round to
see if Philip had arrived.

When Evvie came up with the vet it was clear, even in
the curdling light, that he and Claudia had not merely
never met, but had never clapped eyes on each other
before. The vet knew at once, Claudia knew at once and
Evvie knew at once. So would anyone else who happened to

be watching. Claudia was not the vet's dream in the blue frock, and the vet was not Claudia's man in the Barbour jacket. This man had golden hair turning to red on top of his head, and a thin foxy nose. When he spoke he spoke without any trace of a brogue. 'Glad to meet you,' he said. 'What's your poison?' He had the flat, undistinguished accent of a suburban Londoner.

Evvie, although slightly puzzled by the failure of recognition, was satisfied with this evidence of her creation's vulgarity and nudged Claudia in the ribs.

'How's Gloria?' asked the vet, ladling steaming liquid out of a metal bucket into a paper cup. 'Your mother should let her see a dog. A few whelps'd soon calm her down.'

This man was indubitably common, decided Claudia coldly. The implication behind his words, what he had wished to say, was that any female creature displaying errant behaviour stood simply in need of a good fuck. Claudia accepted the paper cup fastidiously, avoiding any contact with the vet's fingers. Any minute now, she thought, he was likely to wink at her.

'How soon can we go?' she whispered to Evvie.

'Not yet,' said Evvie. 'Drink up your drink. It'll warm you.'

The liquid in the bucket was hot and sweet and tasted innocuous. Claudia accepted a second cup. Someone with a nylon stocking over his face came up and spoke to her. Only he would ever know what he was saying since his voice was muffled and the music was as loud as ever, but Claudia smiled and nodded and sipped her drink. She was beginning to find everything rather fun.

People were roasting potatoes in the outer embers of the bonfire. Roisterers with linked arms hopped in the hot ashes. A man in a wolf mask was burning sausages and meat balls over a bed of charcoal and offering them all round with lewd gestures and inaudible, but doubtless totally predictable, jests.

Claudia didn't mind by now. She felt mellow. She felt that these people were less alien than she had thought, that behind their masks they might be quite familiar to her. When she looked away from the flames she saw Philip standing nearby, leaning against a fence post, and went to him.

'I didn't know you were here,' she said.

'I was here before you,' said Philip. 'I've been on the other side of the fire.'

A sudden gust of wind took the smoke and carried it about her. Claudia turned her head and shivered.

'My love,' said Charles' voice, and Philip kissed her on the mouth.

*

Evvie was looking for the lav. She really was. After several cupfuls she had remarked with tipsy wit that the vet certainly didn't pull his Punches. Now it was beginning to get to her.

She went through the house opening doors. Most of the rooms and passages were lit by central ceiling lights wearing shades of parchment or wicker. Evvie was in too much of a hurry to be sufficiently scornful of them but made a mental note to have a good laugh later. Finally she found a bathroom on the second floor. It was oddly furnished for a bathroom, with a leather armchair beside the bath and a pair of antlers over the door. Oh dear, oh dear, thought Evvie shaking her head in governessy disapproval.

Feeling better, she drifted idly along the landing. A door stood ajar and from within there came sounds of activity. Thinking that during a party every room was laid at the guests' disposal she went in.

Someone said, 'So you've come at last ...'

*

' ... and things that go bump in the night,' said Evvie. She flew out of the front door into the garden. She sped round the bonfire saying 'Claudia, Claudia' under her breath.

Claudia was standing alone with her arms crossed, each hand in the opposite sleeve. 'It's getting cold,' she said. 'Away from the fire it's really quite cold.'

'Claudia,' said Evvie, grabbing her. 'You will *never* believe what I have to tell you. You could never imagine in a million *years* what I've just seen.'

Claudia looked at her abstractedly. She didn't seem to be listening.

'Listen,' said Evvie in a gabble. 'Listen to what I've just seen. I was looking for the lav. Right?'

'Oh Evvie,' said Claudia wearily.

'I *was*,' said Evvie. 'I was. I was. And I went into this room and Fungus – or maybe it was Mango – said they'd been waiting for me ...'

'I told you so,' said Claudia. 'It's your own fault for pestering them all the time. I knew they'd get the wrong idea.'

'No, no, no,' said Evvie. 'They were *all* there. *All* of them. And they hadn't got any clothes on. None at all. They were all absolutely stone stark naked – except they had masks on.'

'They were probably getting ready for bed,' said Claudia.

'*All* of them?' said Evvie. 'All together? There was Bridie and Mango and Clara and Fungus, and Ratface and whatsername in a bat casket – oh hell – *you* know what I mean.'

'I don't see how you could tell,' said Claudia without interest, 'if they were all wearing masks.'

'Oh, I recognised their knees,' said Evvie in a fury. 'Claudia, it was awful. You don't seem to understand.'

'You exaggerate so,' said Claudia.

'Well, you just come and see for yourself,' said Evvie,

pulling at her arm. 'You just come with me and I'll show you.'

'No,' said Claudia, resisting her.

'There you are,' cried Evvie. 'You do believe me. If you didn't believe me you'd come and see.'

'Oh Evvie,' said Claudia. 'I just don't know what to believe any more.'

Evvie let go of her arm and stood looking at her. 'You don't know what you're missing,' she said. 'They look awful. There were candles and umpteen whisky bottles. I can tell you I was out of that door and down those stairs at approximately the speed of light. Where's Philip? I'll make him come and see.'

'I don't know where he is,' said Claudia. 'The last time I saw him he was running round crowned with a pair of antlers. I think he's gone mad.'

'I think everyone's gone mad,' said Evvie. 'I think they've put something in the drink.'

'Let's go home,' said Claudia.

The gate to the field stood open behind them. From what seemed a great distance came the sound of an approaching motor bike. Within seconds Philip rode past them and into the field. They had just time to notice that now he was wearing neither antlers nor the crash helmet. He shot by, like a frenzied charioteer, his vehicle out of control.

'Philip,' yelled Evvie. 'Watch out for my motor bike. You'll ...'

Crash.

Violet lowed.

Claudia screamed and fled through the gate in the direction of the noise.

Evvie screamed too. She screamed: 'Claudia, don't go in that field. Violet's in there.'

But Claudia had no time to be frightened of cows. She felt as she had sometimes felt when the children were small and one of their friends who had come to tea had fallen

146

over. All she knew was that she had had charge of another woman's child and had permitted harm to come to him.

The bike lay on its side, one wheel slowly whirring. Philip was sitting on the ground. He seemed to be alive. Claudia knelt on the muddy grass and moved his hand from the side of his head. There was a swelling already beginning to form.

'I'll take him to the Radcliffe,' she said. 'He may be concussed.'

'You're a bloody fool,' Evvie told Philip. 'If you've totalled my bike you'll have to buy me another one.'

Philip said nothing. He looked dazed. Claudia put her arm round him and led him up the field. Evvie followed, glancing round nervously for signs of Violet.

The bonfire was dying down. Some of the people had removed their masks and were sitting on the ground eating potatoes. They looked quite ordinary now. No one had seemed to notice that anything untoward had happened, and no one said goodbye to them. The music was just as loud.

'Get in the back with Philip, Evvie,' said Claudia, 'and keep an eye on him.'

'I'd like to get my hands on him,' said Evvie. 'He'll have to come back tomorrow and get my bike. Wild oxen wouldn't drag me ...'

'Evvie,' said Claudia.

'Oh, all right,' said Evvie.

Claudia drove slowly and Philip sat with his head in his hands, quite silent.

Evvie was thinking of Horace's hall of mirrors. It seemed to be all right in books: the real thing was something else again. She couldn't stop talking. 'Maybe it's like that thing you read about in the papers,' she said. 'Sort of wife-swapping. They all take their clothes off and close their eyes and move around ...' She speculated aloud on this for a mile or so and then sat for a while sucking the top of her thumb.

147

'Maybe it was group therapy,' she said after another mile had passed. 'Maybe they've got some nutty guru who tells them it's a good idea to whip all their clothes off and let it all hang out ...' She gave a short laugh.

'Oh, give it a rest, Evvie,' said Philip, speaking for the first time.

After another two miles Evvie surmised that they'd all been to the pictures and got the notion of copying an epic orgy. Then on the outskirts of Oxford she concluded that they were a coven of witches. 'I told you I might make Bridie a witch,' she said, 'and look what happened. That's why they chose Hallowe'en and why they had the cats there. I bet Violet was there too. I bet they'd planned to use me as a virgin sacrifice. Well, I'll teach *them*,' she said viciously. 'I'll teach them to play out of their league. I'll put the whole scene in a book with *merciless* descriptions of their horrible persons.'

23

There was the usual late-night collection of losers in the Casualty Ward – damaged drunks glaring with mad eyes at pink elephants, a girl who had taken an overdose, an elderly woman with a sheet wrapped round her foot. There was the usual endless wait while those still capable of thought visualised the doctors idly sipping coffee and discussing their latest conquests.

'I'd better ring Charles and tell him what's happened,' said Claudia. The phone rang and rang but there was no reply.

'He must've gone to bed,' said Claudia. She frowned. 'Evvie, you should ring your mother and tell her why you're so late.'

'Charles is with Mum,' said Evvie, returning. 'I said you'd tried to get him and there was no reply and she said he was there. Then the phone went bleep and I'd got no more money.'

'What's he doing there?' said Claudia. 'How odd. Did you explain Philip wasn't badly hurt?'

'Didn't have time,' said Evvie. 'I only had time to say we'd brought him to hospital.'

'Oh, Evvie, he'll be worried to death,' said Claudia, searching her evening bag for coins. 'I must phone back at once.'

Charles answered at the first ring.

'No, truly Charles, he *is* all right,' said Claudia. 'In the morning he'll be right as rain. It's nothing that a good night's sleep won't cure.' She wondered why she was talking like that. Like a nurse: all bromide and flannel. Probably because Charles did sound as though something huge had stricken him almost to death.

'I told your father you were all right,' said Claudia to Philip, who was still sitting holding his head. 'You are, aren't you?'

'Mm,' said Philip. 'Headache.'

'Serves you right,' muttered Evvie.

A nurse led Philip into a cubicle where a white-coated practitioner lay in wait. She returned with a printed form on a clipboard, prepared to take notes.

'What relation are you?' she asked, head on one side like a bird watching a man dig.

'I'm his mother,' said Claudia.

*

'I'd better get home,' said Charles. 'Claudia said they'd probably be leaving soon, so there's no point in going to the hospital.' He looked older than he had earlier.

'Poor Charles,' said Sylvie. 'But he must be all right or Claudia would've told you.'

'I thought he'd got over all that,' said Charles desperately. 'I thought he'd settled down.'

'He probably has,' said Sylvie. 'It's the first time he's done anything like this since he left Oxford.'

'How do I know that?' asked Charles. 'We have no idea what he's been up to in London.'

'Can't be anything much,' said Sylvie, 'Or you'd have heard.'

She was sorry that Philip had been hurt, but she was glad that Charles had felt it incumbent on him to leave. It had been an exhausting evening. Gloria had run away and been taken by the dog from the lodge in a distant field. By the time Sylvie had floundered and stumbled through thicket and briar, barbed wire and marsh, to the source of all the yelping it was clearly too late to do much about it. Charles who had followed with the torch had turned it on Gloria and her mate, then hastily turned it away. He had offered, without enthusiasm, to return to the cottage for a bucket of water, but Sylvie had pointed out that by the time he'd got back with it all the water would have slopped out again.

Gloria had just come home, wearing the sardonic rictus of a winning dog and looking remarkably cool considering the circumstances. 'Wait till you've got ten children,' Sylvie told her. 'Wait till you've got ten screaming babies to feed and wash. And don't think I'm going to help.' She had an uneasy feeling, that given Gloria's temperament, she would find herself in the role of surrogate mother.

In the morning she met the dog from the lodge. He looked pleased with himself, like a man who thinks himself no end of a dog.

'You can take that look off your face,' said Sylvie. '*I'm* not going to pat you on the back. Don't you imagine Gloria's got any time for you. You're just a puppy-maker, that's what you are.' She wondered how the gamekeeper would react if she demanded puppy maintenance. It was quite true that the possessors of female creatures let themselves in for a great deal of trouble and expense in one way and another.

*

'What *were* you doing at Sylvie's?' asked Claudia curiously. Charles noted with miserable irony that there was no hint of suspicion or jealousy in her voice. His wife considered him far too boring to attract or be attracted by another woman.

'I was lonely,' he said flatly. 'I wanted feminine company and warmth.'

Claudia was astonished. She had never heard Charles speak so before. She decided he must be joking. Sylvie was

151

interesting, but 'feminine' and 'warm' were not the first two words that would occur to you as you thought of her.

Claudia was wearing a bright red frock that Charles had never seen before and bright red lipstick and bright red nail polish. He wanted to tell her to be careful or people would post letters in her, but knew this would be unwise. They were having a late breakfast and Philip was still in bed. Claudia sat at the table and poured her husband more coffee.

'You should've come with us to the party,' she said.

'Yes, you should,' said Evvie, who had stayed the night. She sat down beside Claudia and looked at Charles with marmoset-wide eyes. 'I'd have taken you up to look at them all leaping round in the altogether.'

'You *what*?' said Charles.

'Oh Evvie,' said Claudia. 'She insists she went upstairs, and the vet and all his relations were having a naked orgy,' she told Charles.

'They were,' said Evvie. 'And what's more they expected *me* to join in. They must be *raving*. I don't think people should *ever* take their clothes off. They lose all their dignity and all their identity, and they look horrible. I think everyone should have lots of fur, or maybe feathers. Skin makes me think of plastic bags. Can you *imagine* rolling round with a lot of ghastly naked bodies. *Ergh*.'

Claudia couldn't, but Charles could. He thought it might be rather nice. He put aside this lascivious train of thought. 'If that's true,' he said, 'I think I'd better go round and have a word with them.' It had just occurred to him that they might have planned to include Claudia in their diversions. They had also endangered the life of his eldest son.

'Oh no, you mustn't,' said Evvie. She looked frightened. 'There's something awfully funny about them. Honestly. Somebody kissed me. Kisses are cathartic, they break enchantment. Like death – all those grinning teeth. When they kiss you, you *know* they're a toad.'

Claudia put down her coffee. For the first time she realised that when they had got in last night, Evvie had actually looked rather more shocked than Philip. Perhaps something *had* happened. 'You mustn't go there again,' she instructed Evvie. 'Certainly not on your own.'

'Don't worry,' said Evvie. 'I wouldn't set foot in that house again if they offered me the mortgage.' She shuddered. 'I'll tell you one thing,' she said. 'Fact is a damn sight much more bloody weird than fiction. When I put that in a book nobody'll believe it's true.'

Charles rose, looking purposeful. 'I have to go anyway,' he announced, 'to pick up the bike. I'll borrow a van.'

'Charles, don't go barging in making a fuss,' implored Claudia. 'It's all over now, whatever happened. Let's just forget about it.'

'We'll see about that,' said Charles.

24

Later that day, the Feast of All Saints, Claudia took up
Philip's breakfast on a tray. A baby's breakfast – porridge,
and a boiled egg, and toast cut into soldiers. He was awake.

He looked at her sideways under his lashes. Pale and
bruised, he was as beautiful as the morning. 'Sorry,' he
said.

Claudia smiled at him firmly. 'Foolish creature,' she
said, 'frightening us like that.'

He smiled back, and as she put the tray on his knees, he
ran his fingers up her forearm. Claudia changed her smile.
Translated, it read: 'Oh yes, my dear, we know you're
irresistible, but not to me you're not. Not any longer.'

Momentarily he looked disconcerted. Then he smiled
again. This, too, was a different smile. For a second
Claudia and Philip regarded each other with understanding.

*

Sylvie and Gloria went for a walk in the woods. Already, in
the further depths, frost had bound together the old grasses
and there would be no sun today to loosen them.

'How long are you dogs pregnant for?' Sylvie asked
Gloria, forseeing a snowstorm, the poor beast in travail and
the vet unable to reach them. 'Your timing is lousy. Sensible
animals wait till the roads are clear before they produce
their families.'

Gloria was quite unconcerned. She had forgotten yesterday and had no thought for the morrow.

'You may be right,' said Sylvie. 'Perhaps we'll have a mild winter. There's no point in worrying about it. Then, when spring comes, you can take your children out to play in the long grass.'

*

Charles returned looking annoyed. He wore the air of a man who has planned to sink his knuckles into someone's solar plexus, and has been frustrated. 'They've cleared off,' he said. 'The place was deserted. I found the bike where Philip said, but there's no trace of a cow. No trace of anyone.'

'Perhaps they've dematerialised,' said Evvie dreamily, 'now that I've stopped writing about them.'

'Frightened of the consequences, more likely,' said Charles.

'Can I borrow some writing paper?' asked Evvie. 'I'm going to start another book.'

She wrote: 'Eve drifted slowly along the dimly lit corridor. Her heart-shaped face was pale in the fitful light from the overhead lamps, and her small head rose like a delicate flower from the threadbare cotton dress that covered her slender form. A door stood ajar and from within there came sounds of activity ...'

*

A few weeks later Claudia was sitting sewing by the fire in the drawing-room when she heard a car draw up. 'See who that is, will you, Edith,' she called, breaking off a length of thread, like Ariadne, with her teeth.

Plod, plod, plod went Edith to the hall window. 'It's a dark woman with a big dog,' she yelled back. 'Can't see who it is.'

It might be Amaryllis, thought Claudia. Or it might be Philip's mother come to say that Evvie had won the prize. Or then again it might simply be Sylvie bringing Gloria to see her.

It really didn't matter any more.

MORE ABOUT PENGUINS, PELICANS
AND PUFFINS

For further information about books available from Penguins please write to Dept EP, Penguin Books Ltd, Harmondsworth, Middlesex UB7 0DA.

In the U.S.A.: For a complete list of books available from Penguins in the United States write to Dept DG, Penguin Books, 299 Murray Hill Parkway, East Rutherford, New Jersey 07073.

In Canada: For a complete list of books available from Penguins in Canada write to Penguin Books Canada Ltd, 2801 John Street, Markham, Ontario L3R 1B4.

In Australia: For a complete list of books available from Penguins in Australia write to the Marketing Department, Penguin Books Australia Ltd, P.O. Box 257, Ringwood, Victoria 3134.

In New Zealand: For a complete list of books available from Penguins in New Zealand write to the Marketing Department, Penguin Books (N.Z.) Ltd, Private Bag, Takapuna 9, Auckland.

In India: For a complete list of books available from Penguins in India write to Penguin Overseas Ltd, 706 Eros Apartments. 56 Nehru Place, New Delhi 110019.

A CHOICE OF PENGUINS

☐ *Further Chronicles of Fairacre* **'Miss Read'** £3.95

Full of humour, warmth and charm, these four novels – *Miss Clare Remembers, Over the Gate, The Fairacre Festival* and *Emily Davis* – make up an unforgettable picture of English village life.

☐ *Callanish* **William Horwood** £1.95

From the acclaimed author of *Duncton Wood*, this is the haunting story of Creggan, the captured golden eagle, and his struggle to be free.

☐ *Act of Darkness* **Francis King** £2.50

Anglo-India in the 1930s, where a peculiarly vicious murder triggers 'A terrific mystery story . . . a darkly luminous parable about innocence and evil' – *The New York Times*. 'Brilliantly successful' – *Daily Mail*. 'Unputdownable' – *Standard*

☐ *Death in Cyprus* **M. M. Kaye** £1.95

Holidaying on Aphrodite's beautiful island, Amanda finds herself caught up in a murder mystery in which no one, not even the attractive painter Steven Howard, is quite what they seem . . .

☐ *Lace* **Shirley Conran** £2.95

Lace is, quite simply, a publishing sensation: the story of Judy, Kate, Pagan and Maxine; the bestselling novel that teaches men about women, and women about themselves. 'Riches, bitches, sex and jetsetters' locations – they're all there' – *Sunday Express*

A CHOICE OF PENGUINS

☐ **West of Sunset** **Dirk Bogarde** £1.95

'His virtues as a writer are precisely those which make him the most compelling screen actor of his generation,' is what *The Times* said about Bogarde's savage, funny, romantic novel set in the gaudy wastes of Los Angeles.

☐ **The Riverside Villas Murder** **Kingsley Amis** £1.95

Marital duplicity, sexual discovery and murder with a thirties back-cloth: 'Amis in top form' – *The Times*. 'Delectable from page to page . . . effortlessly witty' – C. P. Snow in the *Financial Times*

☐ **A Dark and Distant Shore** **Reay Tannahill** £3.95

Vilia is the unforgettable heroine, Kinveil Castle is her destiny, in this full-blooded saga spanning a century of Victoriana, empire, hatreds and love affairs. 'A marvellous blend of *Gone with the Wind* and *The Thorn Birds*. You will enjoy every page' – *Daily Mirror*

☐ **Kingsley's Touch** **John Collee** £1.95

'Gripping . . . I recommend this chilling and elegantly written medical thriller' – *Daily Express*. 'An absolutely outstanding storyteller' – *Daily Telegraph*

☐ **The Far Pavilions** **M. M. Kaye** £4.95

Holding all the romance and high adventure of nineteenth-century India, M. M. Kaye's magnificent, now famous, novel has at its heart the passionate love of an Englishman for Juli, his Indian princess. 'Wildly exciting' – *Daily Telegraph*

A CHOICE OF PENGUINS

☐ **Stanley and the Women** Kingsley Amis £2.50

'Very good, very powerful ... beautifully written ... This is Amis *père* at his best' – Anthony Burgess in the *Observer*. 'Everybody should read it' – *Daily Mail*

☐ **The Mysterious Mr Ripley** Patricia Highsmith £4.95

Containing *The Talented Mr Ripley, Ripley Underground* and *Ripley's Game*. 'Patricia Highsmith is the poet of apprehension' – Graham Greene. 'The Ripley books are marvellously, insanely readable' – *The Times*

☐ **Earthly Powers** Anthony Burgess £4.95

'Crowded, crammed, bursting with manic erudition, garlicky puns, omnilingual jokes ... (a novel) which meshes the real and personalized history of the twentieth century' – Martin Amis

☐ **Life & Times of Michael K** J. M. Coetzee £2.95

The Booker Prize-winning novel: 'It is hard to convey ... just what Coetzee's special quality is. His writing gives off whiffs of Conrad, of Nabokov, of Golding, of the Paul Theroux of *The Mosquito Coast*. But he is none of these, he is a harsh, compelling new voice' – Victoria Glendinning

☐ **The Stories of William Trevor** £5.95

'Trevor packs into each separate five or six thousand words more richness, more laughter, more ache, more multifarious human-ness than many good writers manage to get into a whole novel' – *Punch*

☐ **The Book of Laughter and Forgetting**
Milan Kundera £3.95

'A whirling dance of a book ... a masterpiece full of angels, terror, ostriches and love ... No question about it. The most important novel published in Britain this year' – Salman Rushdie

OXFORD WORLD'S CLASSICS

POETICS

ARISTOTLE (384–322 BC), with Plato one of the two greatest philosophers of antiquity, and in the view of many the greatest philosopher of all time, lived and taught in Athens for most of his career. He began as a pupil of Plato, and for some time acted as tutor to Alexander the Great. He left writings on a prodigious variety of subjects, covering the whole field of knowledge from biology and astronomy to rhetoric and literary criticism, from political theory to the most abstract reaches of philosophy. He wrote two treatises on ethics, called *Eudemian* and *Nicomachean* after their first editors, his pupil Eudemus and his son Nicomachus.

SIR ANTHONY KENNY is an Emeritus Fellow of St John's College, Oxford. He is a former Master of Balliol College and Pro-Vice-Chancellor of the University of Oxford and was President of the British Academy from 1989 to 1993. His many books include *The Aristotelian Ethics* (1978), *Aristotle's Theory of the Will* (1979), *Aristotle on the Perfect Life* (1992), and *A New History of Western Philosophy* (2010). For Oxford World's Classics he has also translated *The Eudemian Ethics* (2011).

OXFORD WORLD'S CLASSICS

*For over 100 years Oxford World's Classics have brought
readers closer to the world's great literature. Now with over 700
titles—from the 4,000-year-old myths of Mesopotamia to the
twentieth century's greatest novels—the series makes available
lesser-known as well as celebrated writing.*

*The pocket-sized hardbacks of the early years contained
introductions by Virginia Woolf, T. S. Eliot, Graham Greene,
and other literary figures which enriched the experience of reading.
Today the series is recognized for its fine scholarship and
reliability in texts that span world literature, drama and poetry,
religion, philosophy, and politics. Each edition includes perceptive
commentary and essential background information to meet the
changing needs of readers.*

OXFORD WORLD'S CLASSICS

——

ARISTOTLE

Poetics

——

Translated with an Introduction and Notes by
ANTHONY KENNY

OXFORD
UNIVERSITY PRESS

OXFORD
UNIVERSITY PRESS

Great Clarendon Street, Oxford OX2 6DP
United Kingdom

Oxford University Press is a department of the University of Oxford.
It furthers the University's objective of excellence in research, scholarship,
and education by publishing worldwide. Oxford is a registered trade mark of
Oxford University Press in the UK and in certain other countries

Aristotle translation and editorial material © Anthony Kenny 2013
Additional copyright information appears on pp. xxxix–xl

British Library Cataloguing in Publication Data

Data available

Library of Congress Cataloging in Publication Data

Data available

ISBN 978–0–19–960836–2

Printed in Great Britain by
Clays Ltd, St Ives plc

CONTENTS

INTRODUCTION

The Literary Legacy of Greece

Of all the treasures that ancient Greece has bequeathed to us, its literature is the one that is best preserved. Greek architecture survives in ruins, Greek sculptures have suffered amputations, Greek paintings have almost vanished, and no one really knows how Greek music sounded. However, many masterpieces of literature have survived intact to be read and enjoyed across the centuries. We possess fine specimens of epic and lyric, of tragedy and comedy, of history and philosophy, and of rhetorical and political oratory. Moreover, Greece provided us not only with the earliest European literature, but also with the very earliest literary criticism, to which the present volume bears witness.

Epic was the first genre to be perfected in Greece. The *Iliad* and the *Odyssey* of Homer purport to recount events of the Trojan war of the thirteenth century BC, but they were probably put together in their present form in the eighth century. Perhaps at the end of that century, the poet Hesiod wrote epic texts on agriculture and on the gods of the Greek pantheon. In the late seventh century the poetess Sappho of Lesbos wrote enchanting love lyrics. The most famous Greek lyric poet was Pindar (518–446), who wrote odes in honour of the victors in panhellenic contests such as the Olympic Games.

The most glorious days of ancient Greece fell in the fifth century BC, during fifty years of peace between two periods of warfare. The century began with wars between Greece and Persia, and ended with a war between the city states of Greece itself. In the middle period flowered the great civilization of the city of Athens.

In 499 BC Greeks living in Ionia (now part of Turkey) rose in unsuccessful revolt against the Persian King Darius who ruled over them. Darius invaded Greece to punish those who had assisted the rebels; he was defeated by a mainly Athenian army at Marathon in 490. His son Xerxes launched a more massive expedition in 484, defeated a gallant band of Spartans at Thermopylae, and forced the Athenians to evacuate their city. By 479, however, he had been defeated both at sea (the battle of Salamis) and on land (the battle of Platea). At this point democratic Athens assumed the leadership of the Greek allies and built up a powerful empire of mainland and island communities

The Athenian leader Pericles rebuilt the city's temples which had been destroyed by Xerxes. To this day visitors travel across the world to see the ruins of the buildings he erected on the Acropolis, and the sculptures with which these temples were adorned are among the most treasured possessions of the museums in which they are now scattered. When Pericles' programme was complete, Athens was unrivalled anywhere in the world for architecture and sculpture.

Athens held the primacy too in drama and literature. Aeschylus (525–456), who had fought in the Persian wars, was the first great writer of tragedy: he brought onto the stage the heroes and heroines of Homeric epic, and his re-enactment of the homecoming and murder of Agamemnon can still fascinate and horrify. Aeschylus also represented the more recent catastrophes that had afflicted King Xerxes in his play *Persians*. Younger dramatists, the pious conservative Sophocles (496–406) and the more radical and sceptical Euripides (485–406), set the classical pattern of tragic drama. Sophocles' plays about King Oedipus, killer of his father and husband of his mother, and Euripides' portrayal of the child-murderer Medea not only figure in the twenty-first-century repertoire but also strike disturbing chords in the twenty-first-century psyche. The serious writing of history also began in the fifth century, with chronicles of the Persian wars written by Herodotus (484–425) at the beginning of the century, and Thucydides' (455–400) narrative of the war between the Greeks as the century came to an end.

Philosophy, too, was practised in Periclean Athens, by Anaxagoras (500–428), an early proponent of Big Bang cosmology.

But its golden days were still in the future, with the great trio of Socrates (469–399), Plato (429–347), and Aristotle (385–322). In the Peloponnesian war between Athens and the other Greek cities which brought to an end the Athenian Empire, Socrates served in the Athenian heavy infantry. During the war he displayed conspicuous physical courage, and after it remarkable moral courage in resisting political pressure to carry out illegal acts. This made him unpopular with successive Athenian governments, and he was executed, on trumped-up charges, by the democratic rulers in 399.

Socrates left no writings, and the only portrayal of him in his lifetime was made by Aristophanes (448–380), the greatest writer of Greek comedy, who represents him (in the play *Clouds*) as presiding over a school of chicanery and an academy of bogus research. However, Socrates' philosophical views were preserved and adorned in the dialogues of his pupil Plato, and it is Plato's Socrates who has been the patron saint of philosophy ever since.

Socrates' own interests focused on moral philosophy: what was the nature of virtue, and could it be taught in the way that a craft can be taught? Plato presented a system of moral philosophy with an elaborate metaphysical underpinning, the theory of Forms or Ideas. In his best-known writings he used this theory to solve problems in logic and epistemology as well as in ethics; but in later life he began to see flaws in his system, and to reform it in fundamental ways. Some of the criticisms he set out to answer may have been derived from Aristotle, who was a member of Plato's philosophical school, the Academy, for twenty years.

Aristotle was a polymath: a logician, biologist, zoologist, economist, and political theorist as well as a metaphysician and philosopher of mind. As a moral philosopher, he followed Plato's structuring of the virtues and Plato's emphasis on the close connection between virtue and happiness. But he rejected the theory of Ideas, the metaphysical substructure of Platonic ethics, and developed his own moral theory, presented in magisterial form in two different treatises, the *Nicomachean Ethics* and *Eudemian Ethics*.

In place of the Idea of the Good which was central for Plato, Aristotle offers happiness (*eudaimonia*) as the supreme good with which ethics is concerned, for, like Plato, he sees an intimate connection between living virtuously and living happily. In both ethical treatises a happy life is a life of virtuous activity, and each of them offers an analysis of the concept of virtue and a classification of virtues of different types. One class is that of the moral virtues, such as courage, temperance, and liberality, that constantly appeared in Plato's ethical discussions. The other class is that of intellectual virtues: here Aristotle, unlike Plato, makes a sharp distinction between the intellectual virtue of wisdom, which governs ethical behaviour, and the intellectual virtue of understanding, which is expressed in scientific endeavour and contemplation. The principal difference between Aristotle's two ethical treatises is that one of them regards perfect happiness as constituted solely by the activity of philosophical contemplation, whereas for the other it consists in the harmonious exercise of all the virtues, intellectual and moral.

Philosophy was the last form of literature to reach maturity in classical Greece, but with its arrival literature became for the first time reflective, and conscious of itself. Both Plato's and Aristotle's works contain reflections on the purpose and value of literature. Both philosophers are keenly interested in the relationship between literature and morality, and because they have different conceptions of morality they have different attitudes to literature. In Plato's writings the discussions of literature are scattered, the most interesting of them occurring in his dialogue the *Republic*, which is principally devoted to moral and political philosophy. (These reflections are reprinted in translation in this volume.) Aristotle, however, devoted a self-standing work, the *Poetics*, to the issues that Plato had discussed in fragmented fashion. His brief treatise stands out, therefore, as the first surviving work devoted to literary criticism, and indeed the first essay in the broader field of aesthetics.

Aristotle's Poetics

It is many centuries too late to change the title of this treatise of Aristotle's, but 'Poetics' gives a misleading impression of the contents of the treatise. The Greek word *poiesis* (literally 'making'), as used by Aristotle, has both a narrower and a wider scope than the English word 'poetry'. The *Poetics* treats at length of Greek epic and tragedy, both of which were written in verse; but there were many forms of Greek poetry in which Aristotle shows no interest: didactic treatises like Hesiod's, for instance, or love-lyrics like Sappho's. He was indeed well aware of the distinction between verse and prose, though there was no obvious pair of Greek words to make the distinction. But he is insistent that it is not the metrical form that makes something a poem; it is content rather than form that matters in poetry. The scientific writings of the philosopher Empedocles are not poetry, even though they are composed in hexameters; and if you put the histories of Herodotus into verse they would still be history and not poetry. On the other hand, it is clear to us—if not perhaps to Aristotle—that many of the features that he regarded as essential to epic and tragedy might well find expression in pure prose. If a verse Herodotus would still be history, might not a prose Homer still be what Aristotle calls poetry? After all, most of what the *Poetics* says about the *Iliad* and the *Odyssey* remains true of the numerous prose versions of those works in modern languages.

What English term, then, covers all and only the things that Aristotle calls *poiesis*? 'Imaginative writing' and 'creative writing' come close, but one expression is too clumsy and the other too academic for regular use. The closest modern equivalent to Aristotle's word is the German *Dichtung*, which covers prose fiction as well as verse. In this translation I have decided to retain the traditional translation 'poetry', having prefaced it with this health warning.

The semantic properties of Aristotle's word for poetry mean that his treatise is inadequate as a treatment of Greek verse.

But they confer on it an immense countervailing advantage. Because of them, Aristotle's insights transcend the boundaries of ancient Greek culture and can be applied to creative writing of many ages and many nations. As we shall see in the course of reading the text, the technical concepts he here creates can be applied to novels, dramas, and operas in many languages—even, indeed, to detective stories. Aristotle provides a prism through which different kinds of imaginative writing may be viewed and evaluated.

The *Poetics* concentrates on a single art form: tragedy. Epic is taken seriously, but is given nothing like equal space. A treatment of comedy is promised, but the promise is never fulfilled. The emphasis is entirely intelligible: tragedy was the most fully developed literary product of the time. While seeking to lay bare the essence of tragedy, Aristotle was able to expose, through his close inspection of this single genre, some of the basic principles operative in the creative process itself.

Plato and Aristotle on Poetry

To understand Aristotle's message in the *Poetics* one must know something of Plato's attitude to poetry. In the second and third books of the *Republic* Homer is attacked for misrepresenting the gods and for encouraging debased emotions, and dramatic representation is attacked as deceptive and degrading. In the tenth book Plato's theory of Ideas provides the basis for a further, and more fundamental, attack on the poets. Material objects are imperfect copies of the truly real Ideas; artistic representations of material objects are therefore at two removes from reality, being imitations of imitations (597e). Drama corrupts by appealing to the lower parts of our nature, encouraging us to indulge in weeping and laughter (605d–6c). Dramatic poets must be kept away from the ideal city: they should be anointed with myrrh, crowned with garlands, and sent on their way (398b).

One of Aristotle's aims is to resolve this quarrel between poetry and philosophy. There are three elements in Plato's attack: theological, ethical, and metaphysical. Aristotle has a response to each of them, but he deals with each criticism in a different manner. The metaphysical system of Plato is rejected outright. Poetry is shown to have a significant role within Aristotle's own ethical system. The theological criticism is accepted, but in response tragedy is tacitly secularized.

To understand the vehemence of Plato's attack on epic poetry one must realize that in the Athens of his day the works of Homer enjoyed a status comparable to that of the Bible during much of Christian history. The *Iliad* and the *Odyssey* were a principal source of information about the divine, they contained models for ethical behaviour, and they provided a common source of reference and allusion for the discussion of a wide variety of human interests and values. Plato combines the fervour of a Luther dethroning a debased theology and a David Friedrich Strauss demolishing a mythological farrago.

Plato was not the first philosopher to attack Homer's Olympian gods. Xenophanes had earlier complained that Homer attributed to the gods theft, adultery, deception, and everything that, among humans, would be considered a shame and a reproach. But even if Homer's gods had behaved honourably, they would still resemble humans too much to be credible. Men fashion gods in their own image: Ethiopians believe in gods that are dark and snub-nosed, while the gods worshipped by the Thracians have red hair and blue eyes. 'If cows and horses or lions had hands and could draw, then horses would draw the forms of gods like horses, cows like cows, making their bodies similar in shape to their own.' Instead of this childish anthropomorphism, Xenophanes offered a sophisticated monotheism. He believed in

> One god, lord over gods and human kind
> Like mortals neither in body nor in mind.

Aristotle in the *Poetics* accepts that Xenophanes may well have been right about the nature of the gods; he thinks, however, that Homer can still be defended. But as we shall see later in detail, in his treatment of the great Greek tragedies he pares down to the minimum the divine element they contain.

Both Plato and Aristotle in their ethical systems treated at length of the emotions, and they shared a psychological model in which reasoning and feeling were activities of different parts of the soul, and the intellectual soul was paramount. The role assigned to the emotions was different in the two systems, however. In Plato's virtuous man the expression of emotion would be confined to the minimum. For Aristotle an important part of virtue was the appropriate amount of feeling: there could be too little, as well as too much emotion, in a man's life. In emotion as in action, Aristotle's virtuous person aims at a happy mean. Both philosophers emphasize that there is a close link between poetry and emotion; it is because they have different attitudes to emotion that they have different attitudes to poetry.

As we have seen, a key element in Plato's philosophy was the theory of Ideas. The theory can be characterized as follows. Socrates, Simmias, and Cebes are all called 'men'; they have it in common that they are all men. Now when we say 'Simmias is a man', does the word 'man' stand for something in the way that the word 'Simmias' stands for the individual man Simmias? If so, what? Is it the same thing as the word 'man' stands for in the sentence 'Cebes is a man'? Plato's answer is yes: in each case in which such an expression occurs it stands for the same thing, namely, that which makes Simmias, Cebes, and Socrates all men. This is the Idea of Man, which is something simple, universal, immutable, and everlasting. In general, in any case where the particular things A, B, and C, are all F, Plato is likely to say that they are related to a single Idea of F: they participate in or imitate the Idea. It was on the basis of this theory that Plato complained that works of art were imitations of imitations.

Aristotle rejected the classical theory of Ideas (which, it is fair to notice, was substantially criticized and modified by Plato himself in his later years). The theory, he claimed, fails to solve the problems it was meant to address. It does not confer intelligibility on particular things, because immutable and everlasting Forms cannot explain how particulars come into existence and undergo change. Moreover, the Ideas do not contribute anything to the knowledge of other things or to their being. All the theory does is to bring in new entities equal in number to the entities to be explained: as if one could solve a problem by doubling it. By rejecting the theory, Aristotle undercut the metaphysical objection to poetry.

Aristotle did, however, agree with Plato about the importance of universals; only, he denied that there were any universals separated from individuals. Like Plato, he attached supreme importance to truths that are universal and necessary: they are the province of philosophy. Like Plato, he attaches secondary importance to contingent truths about the empirical world. But he disagrees with Plato about the relative importance of empirical truths and dramatic fictions. Whereas Plato ranked in descending order the disciplines of philosophy, history, and poetry, Aristotle offers a different ranking: philosophy, poetry, and history. He does so on the basis that poetry is more philosophical than history, since it deals with universals rather than particulars.

Representation

Aristotle sites his criticism of Plato within a general theory of imitation or representation. Imitation, he says, so far from being the degrading activity that Plato describes, is something natural to humans from childhood, and is one of the features that makes man superior to animals, since it vastly increases his scope for learning. Secondly, representation brings a delight all of its own: we enjoy and admire paintings of objects that in themselves would annoy or disgust us (1448b5–24).

The Greek word used in this dialogue with Plato is *mimesis*— the word from which our 'mime' is derived. It is often translated 'imitation', and this is indeed appropriate to render Plato's use, since its slightly pejorative overtones would be an expression of Plato's distaste for the activity. But it is not clear that the word is the best English one to render the concept as understood by Aristotle. Several translators simply use the word *mimesis* itself inside an English context. Commonly, the use of transliteration instead of translation is a mark of cowardice in translators. But in this case the difficulty of finding an English word that fits in all the Aristotelian contexts makes one sympathize with those who have given up the task.

Having experimented with several renderings—'mimicry', 'copying', 'portrayal', and 'imitation' itself—I finally opted for 'representation'. In most contexts this is clearly what Aristotle is talking about, and 'representative arts' sounds more natural than 'imitative arts'. What has prevented translators from adopting this version is, I think, the fact that the concept is introduced in connection with the behaviour of children. When a child pretends to be a tiger, or children play at doctors and nurses, it seems a little heavy to say that they are representing something, whereas 'imitation' is quite a natural description of what they are doing. None the less, what they are doing does fall under the concept of representation as sketched by Aristotle, and it is no accident that in English the word 'play' covers both childish pretence and dramatic performance. In the other contexts in which Aristotle uses the word *mimesis*, 'representation' is the English word that comes closest to his sense.

Aristotle begins with a very broad concept of representation. It covers epic, drama, painting, sculpture, dancing, and music. The last two items in this list may give us pause. Dancing, however, fits well enough if we remember that the kind of dances Aristotle would have seen resembled ballets or liturgical processions rather than ballroom dancing. But is music, as such, representational? We do not know enough about Greek music to guess whether Aristotle had in mind something like programme music or rather the imitative effects to be found in Haydn's *Creation* and Beethoven's *Pastoral Symphony*.

At all events, that kind of music would be quickly ruled out by Aristotle's further development of the concept of representation. Forms of representation, he tells us, differ from each other in respect of their medium, their object, and their mode. The broad concept outlined above was hospitable to many media, but when Aristotle moves on to consider object and mode he narrows the concept considerably. The objects of representation, he tells us, are people in action. Thus both comedy and tragedy are representational, differing only in the kinds of people represented; but there is no room for flutes imitating birdsong. Finally, representation may be effected in two different modes, the narrative (as in epic) or the dramatic (as in tragedy). Later, in chapter 24, in the interests of privileging tragedy over epic, Aristotle will even deny that narrative is truly representation; in the *Iliad* only the dramatic speeches really deserve the name. When the concept has been so tendentiously narrowed down from its original scope it begins to lose its utility.

The Natural History of Poetry

In the fourth and fifth chapters of the *Poetics* Aristotle offers a sketch of the development of poetry from the earliest times. First of all, representation took the form of improvised ditties and sketches. The first truly poetical forms were, on the one hand, hymns to gods and panegyrics on heroes, and on the other, lampoons of fools and invectives against knaves. Tragedy developed out of the first kind of poem and comedy out of the second, with Homer as the common ancestor of both.

Tragedy, Aristotle tells us, went through many changes and then ceased to evolve. In its natural condition it has a certain defined length, it involves three actors, it is written in iambic trimeter, and it contains a limited number of choral lyrics. We may feel inclined to smile when we are told that the natural condition of tragedy is precisely the form it took in the works of Sophocles. Indeed, some critics have mocked Aristotle for regarding a human creation such as tragedy as exhibiting any pattern at all of natural evolution and development: this is one more example, they say, of Aristotle's obsession with biology as the model for every scientific discipline. But many respected writers to this day treat human institutions as having a natural history involving a development from primitive to mature forms. It is taken for granted by many political writers in the West, for example, that liberal democracy is the mature form of the state, with monarchy and oligarchy as primitive approximations to, or regressive deviations from, an ideal norm. And while Sophoclean tragedy may not be the one and only mature form of drama, it remains to this day one of the most impressive products of representational art.

Modern scholars tell us that Aristotle's historical account of the development of Greek poetry is inaccurate. Epic, for instance, did not grow out of hymnody and panegyric. The Homeric hymns were no earlier than Homer, and the poets of encomia, such as Simonides and Pindar, wrote considerably later. Defenders of Aristotle say that his treatment is meant to be more schematic than chronological. Those who regard democracy as the ideal form of polity do not contend, after all, that every democracy has reached its maturity by the same route.

The Nature of Tragedy

Aristotle defines tragedy in the following terms:

Tragedy is a representation of an action of a superior kind—grand, and complete in itself—presented in embellished language, in distinct forms in different parts, performed by actors rather than told by a narrator, effecting, through pity and fear, the purification of such emotions. (1449b24 ff.)

Every word in this definition needs careful explanation. Aristotle goes on to offer paraphrases for each of them—except for the most difficult of all, namely *katharsis* or purification. This is the only time the word is used in the *Poetics* and it is never defined. It has been the object of much discussion among commentators, as we shall see. But before contributing to the controversy I will summarize what Aristotle himself has to tell us in expansion of his definition.

Six things, Aristotle says, are necessary for a tragedy: the story, the moral element, the style, the ideas, the staging, and the music. It is the first two of these that chiefly interest him. Stage performance and musical accompaniment are dispensable accessories: what is great in a tragedy can be appreciated from a mere reading of the text. The ideas and the style are more important: it is the thoughts expressed by the characters that arouse emotion in the hearer, and if they are to do so successfully they must be presented convincingly by the actors.

The two things that bring out the genius of a tragic poet are called by Aristotle *muthos* and *ethos*. *Muthos* is often translated 'plot', but it is just the ordinary Greek word for any story, and the *Poetics* has a different expression to denote the plot of a drama, *sustasis pragmatōn*, 'the putting together of events'. *Ethos* is often translated 'character', but this word on its own is inappropriate, since in English everyone who figures in the dramatis personae is a character in the drama, and on the other hand 'character' can also refer to a person's individuality, which is not what Aristotle has in mind. In translation, I have used 'moral element' when Aristotle is talking about the *ethos* of a drama and 'moral character' when he is talking about the *ethos* of a person. It is these two features of tragedy that really interest Aristotle, and he devotes a long chapter to *ethos*, and no less than five chapters to *muthos*.

The protagonist or tragic hero must be neither supremely good nor supremely bad: he should be a person of rank who is basically good, but comes to grief through erring in some serious way. A woman may have the kind of goodness necessary to be a tragic heroine, and even a slave may be a tragic subject. Whatever kind of person the protagonist is, it is important that he or she should have the qualities appropriate to them, and should be consistent throughout the drama. Every one of the dramatis personae should possess some good features: what they do should be in character, and what happens to them should be a necessary or probable outcome of their behaviour.

In Homeric epic the word 'good', applied to a person, can

indicate either social or moral status: it is not always clear whether it indicates power, prowess, or virtue. Echoes of this ambiguity survived into modern times. 'Aristocracy', a word transliterated from the Greek, means etymologically the rule of the best people. In Victorian and Edwardian times to call someone 'a gentleman' might be to compliment him on a particular set of virtues, or simply to indicate the class to which he belonged.

Something of the Homeric ambiguity survives in the *Poetics*. When, in Chapter 14, Aristotle praises Homer for making Achilles a good man and also a paradigm of stubbornness one wonders what moral qualities constitute his goodness, given what is related of him in the *Iliad*. Power, yes, prowess, yes, even, eventually, pity: but virtue? Again, we are told that tragedy deals with people who are 'better than us' and that its plots should deal with noble families: this suggests that tragedy concerns our social betters. But the mention of the goodness of women and slaves shows that it is moral status that is primarily in question. Certainly in his ethical treatises Aristotle is in no doubt that moral virtue is an essential element in human flourishing, whereas noble birth and material wealth are optional extras.

But if it is moral worth that is in question, how far can we accept the principle that every character must have some goodness in them? Should we criticize *Othello* because Iago is bad through and through, or reject *Paradise Lost* because Satan is a protagonist, or condemn *Don Giovanni* out of hand because of its hell-bound hero? Perhaps Aristotle's vision was narrowed because of the tiny number of characters in Greek drama. It is surely much more plausible to claim that every work of fiction should contain some characters with whom we can identify and who have something of goodness within them—though this is not a precept that every modern novelist obeys.

Aristotle insists that in tragedy the most important element of all is story: the characters are created for the sake of the story, and not the other way round. The plot must be a self-contained narrative with a clearly marked beginning, middle, and end; it must be sufficiently short and simple for the spectator to hold all its details in mind. The play must have a unity. You do not make a tragedy by stringing together a set of episodes connected only by a common hero; rather, there must be a single significant action on which the whole plot turns (1451a21–9). Once again, one may query whether Aristotle's point can be generalized to fictions of other kinds: taken literally, his *diktat* would rule out *Don Quixote*, *Tom Jones*, and the *Divina Commedia*. Undoubtedly there is a great difference between a tragic drama and a picaresque novel: but the beneficial effects that Aristotle attributes to tragedy may be achieved in either genre.

As Dorothy Sayers pointed out, in her Oxford lecture reprinted here, many of Aristotle's concepts and precepts concerning plot fit very well a genre which is even further distant from Greek tragedy than the picaresque novel—namely, the detective story. A tragedy must be a unified whole, with a beginning, a middle, and an end, and it must be on an appropriate scale, not too long and not too short. In a typical tragedy, Aristotle tells us, the story gradually gets more complicated until a turning-point is reached, which Aristotle calls a 'reversal' (*peripeteia*). That is the moment at which the apparently fortunate hero falls to disaster, perhaps through a 'discovery' (*anagnorisis*), namely his coming into possession of some crucial but hitherto unknown piece of information (1454b19). The reversal marks the end of the complication (*deesis*) of the plot, which is followed by its explication (*lusis*) in which the twists earlier introduced are gradually unravelled (1455b24 ff.).

The most important of the six elements of tragedy are, then, the story and the morality of the characters. The third item is called by Aristotle *dianoia*—a common Greek word for 'thought', here rendered 'ideas'. By this he means the intellectual element of the dialogue: the thoughts expressed by the characters in offering arguments or reporting facts. *Dianoia* is the expression of the intelligence of the persons in the drama, while the choices they make are the expression of their moral character. *Dianoia* is closely related to the fourth element of tragedy, style (*lexis*), which is the literary quality of its expression.

The fifth element is called by Aristotle *opsis*, which is literally 'visual appearance'; it is often translated 'spectacle'. This, with the sixth element, music, is what makes the difference between attending a performance of a tragedy and merely reading it at home. 'Staging' seems the most appropriate translation— it includes not only the stage-setting but also the visible performance of the actors. Music is treated only summarily in the *Poetics*.

Aristotle's observations are illustrated by constant reference to actual Greek plays, in particular to Sophocles' tragedy *King Oedipus*. Oedipus, at the beginning of the play, enjoys prosperity and reputation. He is basically a good man, but has the flaw of impetuosity. This makes him commit two fatal errors: he kills a stranger in a scuffle, and marries a bride without due diligence. The 'discovery' that the man he killed was his father, Laius, and the woman he married was his mother, Jocasta, leads to the 'reversal' of his fortune, as he is banished from his kingdom and blinds himself in shame and remorse.

This analysis by Aristotle of *King Oedipus* is a striking illustration of the lengths to which he was prepared to go to secularize the plots of Greek dramas. According to the mythology on which Sophocles drew for his play, Laius, having offended the god Apollo, was told that if he fathered a son he would be killed by him. Accordingly, when his son Oedipus was born he was handed over to a servant with orders to kill the child by exposing it. The servant instead gave the baby to a shepherd, who handed him over to the king and queen of Corinth to bring up and treat him as their son. Oedipus, informed by the Delphic oracle that he was destined to kill his father and marry his mother, swore never to return to Corinth where, as he supposed, his parents lived. He went instead towards Thebes, and then fulfilled both the curse and the prophecy by murdering Laius and marrying his widow Jocasta. To a modern reader the most chilling feature of the tragedy is the insistence that no matter what steps you take to thwart it, you must in the end succumb to a divine predestination. One who knew the Oedipus story only from Aristotle would never guess at the importance of this.

Tragedy and Emotion

In Aristotle's account of the moral virtues, as dealt with in books II to V of the *Nicomachean Ethics* and in the second and third books of the *Eudemian Ethics*, the emotions play an important part. 'By emotions', Aristotle tells us (*EE* 1220b11), 'I mean things like anger, fear, shame, desire, and in general anything that as such is generally attended by feelings of pleasure and pain.' The mere occurrence of an emotion does not in itself imply any vice or virtue, but what does indicate character is the relation of emotion to reason. 'What is responsible for whether these emotions occur in accord with reason, or in opposition to it, is states of character: things like courage, temperance, cowardice, intemperance.' The virtues are abiding states, and thus differ from momentary emotions like anger and pity. What makes a person good or bad, praiseworthy or blameworthy, is neither the simple possession of faculties nor the simple occurrence of passions. It is rather a state of character which is expressed both in purpose (*prohairesis*) and in action (*praxis*) (*NE* 1103a11–b25; 1105a19–1106a13; *EE* 1220b1–20).

Virtue is expressed in good purpose, that is to say, a prescription for action in accordance with a good plan of life. The actions which express moral virtue will, Aristotle tells us, avoid excess and defect. A temperate person, for instance, will avoid eating or drinking too much; but he will also avoid eating or drinking too little. Virtue chooses the mean, or middle ground, between excess and defect, eating and drinking the right amount. Virtue is concerned not only with action but also with emotion. An irascible man is one who gets angry more often than he should, and an impassive man gets angry less often than he should.

We may have too many fears or too few fears, and courage will enable us to fear when fear is appropriate and be fearless when it is not. We may be excessively concerned with sex and we may be insufficiently interested in it: the temperate person will take the appropriate degree of interest and be neither lustful nor frigid (1107b1–9).

Since Aristotle's definition of tragedy suggests that its function is to effect a purification of the emotions, it is obviously important to relate what is said in the *Poetics* to the role of the emotions in his general ethical system. But Aristotle's fullest treatment of the emotions occurs not in either of his *Ethics* but in the second book of his *Rhetoric*. Emotions, he says, are feelings that alter people's judgements, and they are accompanied by pain and pleasure. He takes each major emotion in turn, offering a definition of the emotion and a list of its objects and causes. Anger, for instance, he defines as a desire, accompanied by pain, for what appears to be revenge for what appears to be an unmerited slight upon oneself or one's friends. He gives a long list of the kinds of people who make us angry: those who mock us, for instance, or those who stop us drinking when we are thirsty, or those who get in our way at work.

Also those who speak ill of us, and show contempt for us, in respect of the things we most care about. Thus those who seek a reputation as philosophers get angry with those who show disdain for their philosophy; those who pride themselves upon their appearance get angry with those who disparage it, and so on. We feel particularly if we believe that, either in fact or in popular belief, we are totally or largely lacking in the respective qualities. For when we are convinced that we excel in the qualities for which we are mocked, we can ignore the mockery. (1379a32–b1)

Aristotle takes us on a detailed tour of the emotions of anger, hatred, fear, shame, pity, indignation, envy, and jealousy. In each case his treatment is clear and systematic, and often shows—as in the above passage—acute psychological insight.

The statement that tragedy effects, through pity and fear, the purification of these emotions, raises two questions. First, what is it to purify an emotion? Second, why does Aristotle specify just these two emotions of pity and fear?

Aristotle nowhere defines *katharsis*. In his *Politics* (1341b38) he commends musical melodies that achieve *katharsis*, saying that he is using the word without explanation, but that he will give one when he comes to treat of poetry—but he does not keep his promise. The Greek word is a verbal noun related to the adjective *katharos*, which means pure and undefiled. 'Purification' is therefore the most obvious translation, and having considered several others—'purging', 'cleansing', 'refining'—I concluded that it is also the most appropriate. But the word needs careful elucidation if it is not to be misunderstood.

First of all, Aristotle does not mean that tragedy cleanses the soul or purges the emotions, in the sense of getting rid of them altogether. This would be a Platonic rather than an Aristotelian project: according to the doctrine of the mean, feeling too little emotion can be as bad as feeling too much. Nor, I believe, does he mean that tragedy offers a harmless outlet for emotions that might otherwise find their expression in anti-social behaviour. This idea, though championed by some distinguished critics, presupposes an anachronistic, Freudian, hydraulic view of drives that must find some kind of passage from inside us to outside us if there is not to be some psychic explosion.

The translation of *katharsis* as 'refining' is closer to Aristotle's meaning. A courageous man is one who fears what it is right to fear, at the right time, and in the right proportion. Something that adjusts our fears so that they achieve this ideal therefore refines the emotion of fear, and brings it into harmony with reason and virtue. But there is more than this to Aristotle's notion of *katharsis*.

In the paean to the contemplative life that concludes the *Nicomachean Ethics*, Aristotle tells us that that the pleasures of philosophy are the purest of all pleasures (NE 1177a25). From the context it is clear that he is not drawing any link between philosophy and chastity, but rather stressing that the philosopher's pleasures are unmixed with pain. Between his pursuits of pleasure, the libertine suffers the pains of unsatisfied desire; the statesman has to put up with the exertions of public life; but the pursuit of philosophy is—so Aristotle believed—unalloyed pleasure.

This sense of *katharos* must be relevant. In the *Poetics* Aristotle constantly stresses that the emotions are linked to pleasure and pain. Surely, one of the ways in which drama achieves the purification of emotions is that it allows us to experience even the most negative emotions without the pain that accompanies them in real life—we actually enjoy being frightened by what we see on the stage, and the tears we weep over tragic victims are an expression of a grief that is positively sweet. It is the pleasure that we take in feeling these normally depressing emotions that is the pleasure peculiar to tragedy. This is the dramatic counterpart of Aristotle's point that we enjoy seeing pictorial representations of things that in reality we would find ugly and repellent.

Why, finally, does Aristotle, when talking about the purificatory effect of drama, concentrate on pity and fear, rather than, say, love or anger? The obvious answer is that he is focused on tragedy as the paradigm form of drama, and these are the emotions most proper to be evoked by tragedy. In fact, pity and fear should not here be considered as two separate emotions. Watching the travails of Oedipus or Lear, I feel simultaneously pity for the sufferer and fear that I might myself suffer some comparable fate.

However, the very comparison between myself and the tragic hero serves to calibrate the emotions of pity and fear when felt in real life. Watching tragedy helps us to put our own sorrows and worries into proportion, when we observe the catastrophes that have overtaken people who were far superior to the likes of ourselves. Pity and fear, Aristotle continues, are most easily aroused if the tragedy exhibits people as the victims of hatred and murder where they could most expect to be loved and cherished. That is why so many tragedies concern feuds within a single family.

But if pity and fear are the emotions to be taken into account when evaluating the role of tragedy, there is no reason why Aristotle's theory of *katharsis* should not be extended to other emotions when considering other forms of drama or fiction. No doubt Aristotle's own lost treatment of comedy will have explored the relation of the emotions of amusement to the virtue of wittiness or conviviality which he endorses in both of his *Ethics*. The plays of Vàclav Havel that circulated in samizdat served to purify the emotion of anger against communist tyranny, and a reading of *Anna Karenina* may teach us to love wisely rather than too well.

On one point Aristotle seems to have misjudged the relationship between drama and emotion. He tells us that, as far as possible, the poet should act the story as he writes it. People of the same temperament, he says, are more persuasive if they actually feel the emotions they enact: someone actually in distress best acts out distress, someone really angry best acts out rage. Surely this is wrong, both about actors and about poets. The actor who plays the hero does not necessarily act better if he is actually in love with the actress who is playing the heroine. And as for the poet, whatever emotion he may wish to put into his poetry had better be recollected in tranquillity.

Poetry and Truth

The poet's job, Aristotle tells us, is not to relate what actually happened, but rather the kind of thing that *would* happen, either necessarily or probably. In the course of everyday life many events happen contingently, and many things turn out against all probability. History as a whole is full of accidents and unrelated coincidences. A mere chronological narrative will have few lessons to teach us. To be sure, history may help us to discover what are the necessary or probable consequences of different kinds of human action: but to turn these essentially statistical data into a teachable lesson is the task not of the historian but of the poet.

It is thus that Aristotle seeks to defuse Plato's criticism that the poet is at two removes from the truth. The necessary truths of philosophy are, for Aristotle no less than for Plato, truths par excellence, and take precedence over empirical truths. *Historia*, indeed, is Aristotle's general term for truths discovered by empirical inquiry: the results of his own biological investigations—detailed, and often surprisingly accurate—are presented in a treatise that we know as the *Historia Animalium*. But in the *Poetics*, since he is concerned with the dramatic representation of human actions, he takes his examples of *historia* from history proper. The actions of a historic figure exhibit a much greater contingency than the number of feathers on a sparrow or the number of fins on a fish.

Poetry, for Aristotle, has a kind of truth that comes between the necessary truths of philosophy and the contingent particulars of history. It is not for the poet to tell us what Alcibiades actually said or did (or, for that matter, to tell us whether a skylark is or is not a bird). But what the poet has to tell us is of more importance than the details of a politician's career: they are truths that, even if not necessary in the philosophical sense, are universal in their application to human nature. The names of his characters can be used as representative of general types: we are more likely to describe our acquaintances as Eeyores or Uriah Heeps than as Drakes or Cromwells. Thus, in the Olympiad of truth it is poetry that takes the silver medal, while history takes the bronze, and Plato's ranking is reversed.

But is it right to speak of truth at all in connection with tragedy? Is not drama a form of fiction, of creative falsehood, which demands not our belief but only our willing suspension of disbelief? The sophist Gorgias said that tragedy deceives, though he went on to add: 'the deceived are wiser than the undeceived'. And late in the *Poetics* itself Aristotle praises Homer for teaching poets the right way to tell falsehoods

At this point we need to distinguish not two but three kinds of truth and falsehood that come into play when we compare history and drama. It is easier to explain this in terms of English tragedy, since we do not know what Aristotle thought was the historical truth about King Oedipus. So let us consider, for a moment, Shakespeare's *Macbeth*. (The play fulfils most of Aristotle's criteria for a good tragedy, though he would have thought that there was too much supernatural intervention in the shape of witches and ghosts.) The historical king of Scotland, we are told, bears very little relation to the character of Macbeth in the play. But this kind of falsehood does not matter in the least; we do not go to the theatre to be informed about the murky early history of Scotland. At this level, what Sir Philip Sidney says is correct: 'the poet nothing affirmeth and therefore never lieth'.

None the less, in most works of fiction there are passages where the author does set out deliberately to deceive his audience or his readers. This is most conspicuous in the case of mystery stories, where the reader is to be led up the garden path until the last moment. But many such passages occur in Shakespeare too: in *Macbeth*, when Malcolm pretends that he will be a tyrant if chosen as king; and at the beginning of *Lear*, where the audience is led to believe that Regan and Goneril are loving daughters. This, we might say, is a second level of dramatic falsehood, and it is with this kind of thing in mind that Aristotle compliments Homer on his skill in deceiving the audience. The deception, of course, does not imply any moral fault on the part of the author, since it is always removed before the end of the fiction.

There remains the third, upper level of truth and falsehood: the universal generalizations about human nature, human character, and human action. These are not necessarily uttered on the stage in the drama (though they often figure in the choruses of Greek tragedy), but they are the lessons that the drama explicitly or implicitly seeks to draw. Aristotle insists that such lessons must be based on necessity or probability. The lessons that drama teaches may be the same as those that a moral philosopher might teach, but—as Sidney emphasizes, and as is implicit in Aristotle's insistence on the link between tragedy and pleasure—drama teaches us in a manner that motivates us, in a way that chill moral truisms do not.

But if drama can teach moral truth in an inspiring way, can it not just as well teach moral error? Of the apologists for poetry represented in this volume, the one to face up most candidly to this difficulty is Shelley. Shelley makes clear the possibility of a false ideology being promoted by a great work of literature. *Paradise Lost* was written to support a system of Christian theology which, as an atheist, Shelley thought false and corrupting. But somehow, he claims, genius forces Milton's poem to be a refutation of that very system.

Milton's Devil as a moral being is as far superior to his God, as one who perseveres in some purpose which he has conceived to be excellent, in spite of adversity and torture, is to one who in the cold security of undoubted triumph inflicts the most horrible revenge upon his enemy, not from any mistaken notion of inducing him to repent of a perseverance in enmity, but with the alleged design of exasperating him to deserve new torments. Milton has so far violated the popular creed (if this shall be judged to be a violation) as to have alleged no superiority of moral virtue to his God over his Devil. And this bold neglect of a direct moral purpose is the most decisive proof of the supremacy of Milton's genius.

Shelley's ingenious defence surely fails. Christianity is either true or false. If it is true, then *Paradise Lost* can be corrupting precisely because of its deifying of Satan; if it is false, then it can be corrupting because it accepts principal elements of the Christian system.

It was not until the nineteenth century that aestheticians presented detailed arguments for the conclusion that art could not be great unless it was morally good. One such was John Ruskin, and another was Leo Tolstoy. For Ruskin, artistic creation was a demanding matter, and the demands made by art could be justified only by the seriousness of its moral purpose: namely, to reveal fundamental features of the universe. The experience of beauty, he maintained, arises from a truthful perception of nature, and leads on to an apprehension of the divine. Only if an artist is himself a morally good person will he be able to deliver this revelation in an incorrupt form, and set before us the glory of God. Ruskin applied his moralizing theory of art to two arts in particular: painting and architecture. He accepted Aristotle's parallel between painting and poetry: painting, for him, was essentially a form of language: technical skill was no more than mastery of the language, and the worth of a painting depended on the value of the thoughts that it expresses.

For Tolstoy too, art can be good only if it has a moral purpose. He rejected the idea that the aim of art is beauty and that beauty is recognized by the enjoyment it gives. The real purpose of art, he maintained was communication between human beings. While rejecting the romantic idea that art must give pleasure, he agreed with Wordsworth that its essence was the sharing of emotion. The feelings with which these works of art infect us may be good or bad. Art is only good if the emotions it injects are good; and those emotions can be good only if they are fundamentally religious and contribute to a sense of universal human brotherhood. The emotions to be communicated by art must be emotions that can be shared by mankind in general, and not just by a pampered elite. Where this is not the case we have either bad art or pseudo-art. Tolstoy is willing to accept that this judgement condemns many of the most admired works of music and literature—including his own novels. The greatest novel of the nineteenth century, he maintained, was *Uncle Tom's Cabin*, which spread the message of universal brotherhood across the boundaries of race and class.

In the twentieth century the moralistic view of art quickly became unfashionable. Art, many held, should be autonomous, and a work of art might be good art, and even great art, while being morally or politically deleterious. Aristotle does indeed say in the *Poetics* that the standard of correctness in poetry is not the same as that in ethics, but he would have totally rejected the idea that the poet has no ethical responsibility. Art for art's sake is far removed from Aristotle's aesthetic theory. It might, indeed, have been thought to be at the furthest extreme, had it not been that Nietzsche had already claimed that art was not only autonomous from, but supreme over, morality.

Advice to the Practising Poet

In most of the *Poetics* Aristotle seems to be addressing himself to dramatic audiences rather than to dramatists. Some of the information he offers is rather mundane: the list of the order of scenes and songs in Chapter 12, for instance, would be of use principally to a first-time theatregoer. It is comparable to telling someone about to hear for the first time a Mass by Mozart or Haydn that the Gloria comes after the Kyrie but before the Creed. But most of the time he has loftier purposes: to bring home to members of the audience how they should react to what they see and hear, and what they should hope to get out of the experience.

In later chapters, however, Aristotle offers practical advice to playwrights, particularly about the construction of their plots. Here again, some of the information offered operates at a basic level: Chapter 20 is of more interest to the grammarian or the historian of linguistics than it would be to any moderately competent dramatist about to put pen to paper. But the inclusion of such material is consistent with Aristotle's down-to-earth view of imaginative writing. The poet, in his view, is neither inspired nor engaged in self-expression: the nearest he comes to any such romantic view is the throwaway remark that to be a poet you must be either a genius or a madman. His considered opinion is that a poet is a craftsman, as befits the name of his trade; for *poiesis* in Greek is literally 'making'. Consequently, the advice that he offers is concrete and technical, about the choice of characters to represent and the internal structure to give to the plot.

The hero should be a person of such and such a kind, belong to such and such a social class, suffer at the hands of those close to him. There should be a turning-point in the plot, a reversal of fortune consequent upon the discovery of some crucial but hitherto unknown fact. Preferably the reversal of fortune should be from prosperity to adversity. If the story has an end that is happy for some characters, there must be countervailing suffering for others.

It is notable that every word of the advice in the previous paragraph could be applied without alteration to fictions of very various kinds. Jane Austen's novels deal, in her own words, with '3 or 4 families in a Country Village', far removed from the royal families of Mycenae and Thebes. Yet every one of her novels contains a discovery and a reversal—often more than one. In *Pride and Prejudice*, for example, Elizabeth Bennet's discovery that her sister has eloped with the unprincipled Wickham leads to a reversal in the relationship between Mr Darcy and herself. In *Sense and Sensibility* Edward's discovery that his unwanted fiancée Lucy has switched her affections leads to his happy union with Elinor Dashwood. The novels have happy endings, which exclude them from Aristotle's favourite class of story, but they are endings of the tolerable kind, like that of the *Odyssey*, in which, as he says, there are different endings for the better and worse characters. The transitions from adversity to prosperity in Austen's works are, of course, always transitions in respect of eligibility as a marriage partner, and Aristotle would be disappointed that no one gets killed.

Aristotle's remarks on style are naturally much more tied to the Greek context than his guidelines on content, and few of them are likely to be helpful to twenty-first-century writers in English. He invented one device, however, which remains popular among teachers and critics of literature today: change one word in a line of a canonical author, and see what effect this has on the impact of the verse.

Finally, we come to the musical element. Though in his *Politics* Aristotle offers his opinion about the different emotional effects of different musical modes, he has very little to say about music in the *Poetics*, or even about the lyrical poetry which the music accompanies. Among modern art forms it is, of course, opera that most closely resembles Greek tragedy, particularly operas such as *The Magic Flute* and *Carmen*, where aria and chorus are interspersed with spoken passages as well as recitative. The one piece of advice that Aristotle offers remains useful: the chorus should not just stand about and sing but should take part in the action. It is this feature, among others, that makes Verdi's later operas preferable to his early ones.

The Afterlife of the Poetics

The *Poetics* is essentially a series of lecture notes, and it is much to be regretted that we do not possess a second book devoted to comedy. Nothing in the rest of Aristotle's *Nachlass* compensated for its loss. Substantial fragments survive of his dialogue *On the Poets*, but in spite of devoted scholarly efforts to piece them together, they do not add much, apart from some gossip about Homer, to the content of the *Poetics*.

The Aristotelian corpus, in addition to the systematic scientific treatises, contains a massive collection of occasional jottings on scientific topics, the *Problems*. From its structure this appears to be a commonplace book in which Aristotle or someone else wrote down provisional answers to questions that were put to him by his students or correspondents. The collection contains many fascinating details that give insight into the workings of his omnivorous intellect. The *Problems* let us see Aristotle with his hair down, rather like the 'Table Talk' of later writers.

The eighteenth book of the *Problems* is concerned with issues connected with literature. It begins with a question that is particularly endearing to those who may have found it hard to read their way through Aristotle's more difficult works. 'Why is it that some people, if they begin to read a serious book, are overcome by sleep even against their will?' (916b1). Most of the problems discussed concern rhetoric rather than poetry, but two questions are raised that are relevant to the topics of the

Poetics. Why, we are asked, do we feel more pleasure in listening to narratives in which the attention is concentrated on a single point than in hearing those which are concerned with many subjects? The answer offered is that what is definite is more easily understood than what is indefinite. Why, again, do we like to hear of events which are neither very old nor quite new? We are told in answer, 'We disbelieve events which occurred before our time, and we take no pleasure in events which we disbelieve. Recent events, on the other hand, are still as it were before our eyes and so we take no pleasure in hearing of them.' This seems naive in comparison with the elaborate theory of the pleasures of suspending disbelief in drama that we are offered in the *Poetics.*

The history of the *Poetics* in late antiquity is obscure, as is that of so many of Aristotle's works. The treatise appears in the list of his work in the life of Aristotle by Diogenes Laertius (*c.* AD 200–50), and some of the ideas it contains surface in the *Ars Poetica* of the Roman poet Horace, writing in the time of Augustus. But from then until the Renaissance it leaves little trace. Like other works of Aristotle, it was known to Islamic scholars before it was read by medieval Latins. The twelfth-century Cordoban philosopher Averroes commented on it, and one of his commentaries was translated into Latin in 1256. The *Poetics* itself was translated from the Greek by Aquinas' collaborator William of Moerbeke in 1278; but his translation soon disappeared from view, and did not resurface until the twentieth century. Scholastic lack of interest in the *Poetics* is easy to understand: there was nothing in medieval culture that resembled at all closely Greek tragedy or comedy. In our own time, the novelist Umberto Eco has built an exciting historical novel, *In the Name of the Rose*, around the fiction of the survival and eventual destruction of a second book of the *Poetics* in a medieval conventual library.

The revival of Greek scholarship among Renaissance humanists brought with it a renewal of interest in the *Poetics*. In 1498 there appeared a Latin translation by Giorgio Valla, and the Greek original was printed in 1508. In 1536 the work was fairly launched on to the learned world by Alessandro de' Pazzi, in an edition with parallel Greek and Latin texts. But the Renaissance understanding of the work was flawed. Humanists prized rhetoric above philosophy as it had been understood in the Middle Ages, and they treated the *Poetics* as fundamentally a work of rhetoric. This was directly contrary to Aristotle's own conception, in which rhetoric and poetry were two quite distinct disciplines: rhetoric being the value-neutral art of persuasion, while poetry was an important contribution to the moral education of the human person.

The Italian humanist Ludovico Castelvetro published in 1576 a text of the *Poetics* with a translation and commentary. He blew up Aristotle's remarks on unity and scale into a doctrine of the Three Unities, of time, place, and action. The action of the drama should not last longer than the time of its performance, and the scene should not be changed throughout the play. The principles he set out could only dubiously claim the backing of Aristotle, but they had a great influence on the classical French tragedies of Corneille, and through him, on English Restoration dramatists such as John Dryden.

In the sixteenth century the most fruitful contribution to the understanding of the *Poetics* was made not by any of the learned humanist commentators on the text, but by a practising poet: Sir Philip Sidney. Sidney, a scholar and courtier who became governor of Flushing in 1585 and was killed by a Spanish bullet in gallant circumstances at the battle of Zutphen a year later, left behind a number of poetical works, of which the most famous is the sonnet sequence *Astrophel and Stella*. Sidney was perhaps the first writer since Aristotle to provide a seriously considered answer to Plato's criticism of poetry and drama. He saw poetry as a force superior to rhetoric, history, and even philosophy, since it can bring the reader to tune his passions to the highest pitch of motivation to well-doing. Perceptive passages from his *Apology for Poetry* are included in this volume.

In using Aristotle's text to defend poetry against Platonic accusations, Sidney was the first of a long line of poets and literary critics. In the preface to *Samson Agonistes* Milton invoked Aristotle in support of the respectability of tragedy, quoting his claim that it had 'power by raising pity and fear, or terror, to purge the mind of those and such-like passions, that is to temper and reduce them to just measure with a kind of delight'. There followed Dryden's *Essay of Dramatic Poesy* and Shelley's *Defence of Poetry*, while Samuel Johnson's *Preface to Shakespeare* contains Aristotelian elements.

Shelley, a radical who was expelled from Oxford for writing on the necessity of atheism, wrote his best poems after eloping with Mary Godwin in 1814. His masterpiece, *Prometheus Unbound*, was written in Pisa in 1819, along with a number of shorter poems familiar to generations of schoolchildren, such as 'Ode to the West Wind' and 'To a Skylark'. Having written *Adonais*, an elegy on the death of Keats in 1821, he was himself drowned off Livorno in the following year. He was moved to take up his pen in defence of poetry by an essay of Thomas Love Peacock, *The Four Ages of Poetry*, which had argued that the best minds of the future should devote themselves to the social sciences rather than to literature. In response Shelley worked up some Aristotelian themes, as can be seen in the extract printed in this volume, though he went beyond Aristotle in his final triumphant claim that poets are the unacknowledged legislators of the world.

Until comparatively recently, Aristotle's *Poetics* was of more interest to students of literature than to students of philosophy, and Ingram Bywater's 1909 translation was read more often in English departments than in departments of Classics. Interest in it, indeed, spread to the general literary intelligentsia with little philosophical investment, as is illustrated by the here reprinted public lecture of Dorothy L. Sayers, best known for her crime novels featuring Lord Peter Wimsey and her verse translation of Dante. In recent years, however, several scholars—most notably Stephen Halliwell in a series of studies—have shown the importance of reading the *Poetics* as a significant part of Aristotle's ethical system. In offering this new translation, I have tried in particular to bring out the relationships between Aristotle's literary criticism and his moral philosophy.

NOTE ON THE TEXTS AND TRANSLATIONS

The text of the *Poetics* I have translated is that presented in the Oxford Classical Texts series, edited by Rudolf Kassel (Oxford: Clarendon Press, 1965). In some places where Kassel marks a lacuna or obelizes a passage I have accepted the conjectures of other scholars.

In translation I have not attempted to reproduce the order of words or clauses in the Greek manuscripts, or the punctuation of the OCT editor. I have aimed to produce clear and readable English that preserves Aristotle's sense, rather than to achieve word-for-word correspondence with the original. The decisions I made about the translation of key words in the vocabulary are recorded in the Glossary.

The numbering system, with references such as 1214a1, is that nowadays universally adopted: it derives from Immanuel Bekker's 1831 Berlin edition of Aristotle's works. The marginal numbers correspond to those of the Greek text, so that occasionally in the translation the correspondence is not exact. I have also noted the division into chapters in the Bekker text, which does not always correspond to the division into sections which seemed most appropriate in the translation.

The passages from Plato's *Republic* are taken from the translation by D. A. Russell in the Oxford World's Classics volume *Classical Literary Criticism* (Oxford, 1989), and reprinted by permission. They are also numbered, as is standard practice, in accordance with the pagination of the sixteenth-century Stephanus edition, with letters to mark subdivisions of the pages.

Sidney's *Apology for Poetry* was published in 1595 in two editions. One, by Ponsonby, was entitled *The Defence of Poesy*; it is the other, by Olney, that is reproduced here.

Shelley's *Defence of Poetry*, though written in 1821, was first published in 1840 in *Essays, Letters from Abroad, Translations and Fragments*, edited by Shelley's widow.

'Aristotle on Detective Fiction' was a lecture delivered by Dorothy L. Sayers in Oxford on 5 March 1935, first published in 1936 and later reprinted in *Unpopular Opinions* (London: Gollancz, 1946). It is here reprinted by kind permission of the estate of Dorothy L. Sayers.

I am greatly indebted to previous translators into English of the *Poetics* and I found particularly helpful the works of Ingram Bywater, Malcolm Heath, Stephen Halliwell, and Margaret Hubbard. For comments on, and amendments to, my own translation I owe a great debt of gratitude to Jill Paton Walsh and to my wife Nancy Kenny.

SELECT BIBLIOGRAPHY

Most of Aristotle's works appear in the original Greek in volumes of the Oxford Classical Texts series, and many of them appear with a translation in volumes of the Loeb Classical Library. All of the surviving works are to be found in English in the two-volume Oxford Translation, edited by J. Barnes (Princeton: Princeton University Press, 1984). The Clarendon Aristotle series (Oxford, Clarendon Press, 1963–) contains translations of selected texts, with detailed philosophical notes. Many of Aristotle's works are available in translation in Penguin Classics or in Oxford World's Classics.

On Aristotle in general, the following works can be recommended:

Barnes, J., *Aristotle* (Oxford: Oxford University Press, 1982).

—— *The Cambridge Companion to Aristotle* (Cambridge: Cambridge University Press, 1995).

—— *Aristotle: A Very Short Introduction* (Oxford: Oxford University Press, 2000)

Shields, C., *Aristotle* (London: Routledge, 2007).

On Aristotle's *Poetics* and Ethics

Broadie S., and Rowe, C., *Aristotle, Nicomachean Ethics*, trans., introduction and commentary (Oxford: Oxford University Press, 2002).

Bywater, Ingram, *Aristotle on the Art of Poetry* (Oxford: Clarendon Press, 1909).

Halliwell, Stephen, *Aristotle's Poetics* (London: Duckworth, 1986; 2nd edn. 1998).

House, Humphrey, *Aristotle's Poetics* (London: Rupert Hart-Davis, 1956).

Irwin, T. H., *The Development of Ethics*, volume 1 (Oxford: Oxford University Press, 2007).

Kenny, A., *Aristotle on the Perfect Life* (Oxford: Oxford University Press, 1992).

Nussbaum, Martha, *The Fragility of Goodness: Luck and Ethics in Greek Tragedy and Philosophy* (Cambridge: Cambridge University Press, 1986).

Rorty, A. O. (ed.), *Essays on Aristotle's Poetics* (Princeton: Princeton University Press, 1992).

Translations of the Poetics

Ingram Bywater's translation is available in the second volume of the Barnes edition cited above.

Halliwell, Stephen, *Aristotle: Poetics*, Loeb Classical Library (Cambridge, Mass.: Harvard University Press, 1995).

Heath, Malcolm, *Aristotle: Poetics* (Harmondsworth: Penguin Books, 1996).

Hubbard, Margaret, 'Aristotle: *Poetics*', in D. A. Russell and M. Winterbottom, *Classical Literary Criticism*, Oxford World's Classics (Oxford: Oxford University Press, 1972).

Further Reading in Oxford World's Classics

Aristotle, *The Eudemian Ethics*, trans. Anthony Kenny.

—— *The Nicomachean Ethics*, trans. David Ross, revised and edited by Lesley Brown.

—— *Politics*, trans. Ernest Barker, rev. R. F. Stalley.

—— *Physics*, trans. Robin Waterfield, ed. David Bostock.

Milton, John, *The Major Works*, ed. Stephen Orgel and Jonathan Goldberg.

Plato, *Republic*, trans. Robin Waterfield.

Ruskin, John, *Selected Writings*, ed. Dinah Birch.

Shelley, Percy Bysshe, *The Major Works*, ed. Zachary Leader and Michael O'Neill.

Sidney, Sir Philip, *The Major Works*, ed. Katherine Duncan-Jones.

A CHRONOLOGY OF ARISTOTLE

(All dates are BC)

399   Trial and death of Socrates in Athens; Plato was around 30 at the time.

384   Aristotle born in Stagira, northern Greece. His father is doctor at the court of Macedon.

367   Aristotle goes to study in Athens, joins Plato's Academy.

347   Death of Plato, whose nephew Speusippus succeeds him as head of the Academy. Aristotle leaves Athens. He travels to Asia Minor and marries Pythias, the daughter of Hermias, who hosts him in Assos, Asia Minor.

342   Aristotle becomes tutor to Alexander, son of Philip II of Macedon.

338   Battle of Chaironeia, at which Philip II defeats Thebes and Athens, and becomes master of the Greek world.

336   Death of Philip; he is succeeded by his son Alexander.

335   Aristotle returns to Athens and founds his own 'school' the Lyceum. After the death of his wife he lives with a slave-mistress, Herpyllis, by whom he has a son, Nicomachus.

323   Death of Alexander; anti-Macedonian feeling prompts Aristotle to leave Athens.

322   Death of Aristotle at Chalcis in Euboia.

OUTLINE OF THE *POETICS*

I. THE VARIOUS KINDS OF POETRY

II. THE NATURE OF TRAGEDY

III. EXCELLENCE IN TRAGEDY

PLATO

REPUBLIC

Plato on poetry
1) too emotional, not logical
2) removed imitation
3) goals

From *Republic*, Books 2 and 3

'We must begin by controlling the fable-makers, and admit only 377b
the good fables they compose, not the bad. We shall then persuade nurses and mothers to tell children the admitted fables, c
and mould their minds with fable much more than they now
mould their bodies with the hand. Most of the tales they tell
now will have to be thrown out.'

'Which?'

'If we look at the big fables, we shall also see the little ones.
Big and little need to be of the same type and have the same
effect. Don't you agree?' d

'Yes: but I don't see what you mean by the big ones.'

'Those that Hesiod and Homer told, and the other poets. For
it's the poets who told men, and still tell them, the false stories
they themselves compose.'

'What stories? And what fault do you find with them?'

'The fault one must find, first and foremost, especially when
someone tells falsehoods wrongly.'

'But what is it?'

'Making bad verbal likenesses of gods and heroes—just e
like a painter making a picture unlike the object he wants to
paint.'

'Well, it's certainly right to find fault with that sort of thing.
But just what do we mean?'

'To begin with, the greatest falsehood, involving the greatest
issues, was wrongly told by the person who said that Ouranos
did what Hesiod said he did, and that Kronos took his revenge
upon him.* What Kronos did and what happened to him at 378
his son's hands is something I should not want to be told without precaution to the young and foolish, even if it had been
true. If possible, it should have been veiled in silence; but if
there had been great need to tell it, it should have been made
a secret, for as small an audience as possible—and they should

3

have had to sacrifice not a pig,* but some expensive and inaccessible victim, so that as few people as possible should hear the tale.'

'These stories are indeed difficult.'

b   'They are not to be repeated in our city, Adimantus. Nor is it to be said in a young man's hearing that if he committed the most outrageous crimes, or chastised an erring father by the direst means, he would be doing nothing remarkable, but only what the first and greatest of the gods have done.'

'I don't myself think that these are suitable stories.'

'It's the same with all the tales of how gods war, plot, and
c fight against gods—not that they're true anyway—if our future city-guardians are to believe that readiness to hate one another is the greatest scandal. Still less must they be told elaborate fables of battles of giants, and all the other various hostilities of gods and heroes towards their kith and kin. If we are somehow to convince them that no citizen has ever been the enemy of another, nor is it right that he should be, then *that* is the lesson
d that older men and women must impress on the children from the start, the lesson (more or less) that poets too must be forced to impress on the adult population. Hera tied up by her son, Hephaestus thrown out by his father because he was proposing to defend his mother against a beating, Homer's battles of gods—all this is inadmissible, whether it was composed allegorically or not. Young people can't distinguish the allegorical from the non-allegorical, and what enters the mind at that age
e tends to become indelible and irremovable. Hence the prime need to make sure that what they first hear is devised as well as possible for the implanting of virtue.'

'That makes sense. But if we were to be asked what these things are, what the stories are, what should we say?'

'You and I, Adimantus, are not poets, at the moment: we are
379 founders of a city. Founders have to know the patterns within which poets are to be made to construct fables, and beyond which they must not be allowed to go, but they don't have to make up fables themselves.'

4

'True enough: but just what *are* the patterns for an account of the gods?'

'Something like this, I fancy. God must always be represented as he is, whether in epic or in lyric or in tragedy.'

'Yes indeed.'

'Now God is in truth good and must be so described.'   b

'Of course.'

'And nothing good is harmful, is it?'

'No.'

'Does the non-harmful harm?'

'No.'

'And does what doesn't harm do any evil?'

'No.'

'And what does no evil is cause of no evil?'

'Of course.'

'Now again. The good is useful?'

'Yes.'

'Therefore the cause of felicity?'

'Yes.'

'The good therefore is not the cause of everything, but only of what is well.'

'Certainly.'   c

'God, therefore, being good, cannot be responsible for every-thing, as is the common opinion, but only of some things in human life. There is much for which he bears no responsibility. Our blessings are far fewer than our troubles, and while none but God is responsible for the blessings, we must seek other causes for the troubles.'

'That seems perfectly right.'

'We must therefore not allow Homer or any other poet to make foolish mistakes about the gods.' [...]   d

'The subject of men remains.'   392a

'Clearly.'

'Well, we can't legislate for that at the moment.'

'Why not?'

'Because, I imagine, we shall say that poets and prose-writers
b make serious bad statements about men—that there are many
unjust men who are happy and just men who are miserable,
that secret wrongdoing is profitable, that justice is the good of
others and our own loss—and so on. We shall have to forbid
them to say this, and command them to compose songs and
fables to the opposite effect.'

'I'm sure we shall.'

c 'Then if you agree I am right, shall I say that you have agreed
to what we have long been seeking?'

'Yes, that's right.'

'Then we shall come to our agreement that this is the sort
of thing to be said about men only when we have discovered
what justice is, and what is its natural advantage to its possessor,
whether or not he *appears* just.'

'True.'

'So much for what is said. We must next consider its expression. When that is done we shall have covered the whole subject
of what is to be said and how.'

'I don't understand what you mean.'

d 'You ought to; but perhaps you'll know better if I put it like
this. Everything that fable-tellers or poets say is a narrative of
past or present or future.'

'Of course.'

'And they execute it either by simple narrative or by narrative conveyed by imitation (*mimēsis*) or by both.'

'I should like a clearer account of that too, please.'

'I must be a ridiculously obscure teacher. I'll try to do
what incompetent speakers do and show you what I mean by
e taking a little bit, and not the whole topic. Tell me: you know
the beginning of the *Iliad*, where the poet says that Chryses
asked Agamemnon to release his daughter, Agamemnon was
393 angry, and Chryses, unsuccessful, cursed the Achaeans to the
god?'

'I know.'

'Then you know as far as the lines

and he begged all the Achaeans,
and especially the two Atridae, the generals of the host,*

the poet speaks in his own person, and does not try to turn
our attention in another direction by pretending that someone
else is speaking. But from this point on he speaks as though he
were Chryses himself and tries to make us think that it is not
Homer talking, but the old priest. And he does practically all b
the rest of the narrative in this way, both the tale of Troy and
the episodes in Ithaca and the whole *Odyssey*.'

'Yes.'

'Now it is narrative both when he makes the various speeches
and in the passages between the speeches.'

'Of course.'

'But when he makes a speech pretending to be someone else, c
are we not to say that he is assimilating his expression as far as
possible to the supposed speaker?'

'Certainly.'

'And to assimilate oneself in voice or gesture to another is to
imitate him?'

'Yes.'

'So in this sort of thing Homer and the other poets are con-
veying their narrative by way of imitation (*mimēsis*)?'

'Yes.' [...]

'We must come to an understanding as to whether we are to 394d
allow our poets to narrate by imitation, or partly by imitation
(and if so, what parts), or not to imitate at all.'

'I have an inkling that you are asking whether we should admit tragedy and comedy into the city or no.'

'Perhaps—or perhaps more than that. I don't know yet: we
must go where the wind of argument blows.'

'That's right.'

'Well, then, consider whether our guardians ought to be imi- e
tative people or not. Or does this follow from our previous argument that an individual can do one thing well but is liable to

fail in everything, so far as acquiring real note is concerned, if he tries to do many things?'

'Bound to follow.'

'Similarly with imitation—one individual can't imitate many things well, though he can one?'

'Yes.'

'So still less will one man be able to pursue some worthwhile pursuit and also imitate many things and be an imitator. Even 395 apparently closely related imitations cannot be practised well by the same person—tragedy and comedy for example. You called these two imitations, didn't you?'

'Yes; and you're quite right, the same people can't do both.'

'Nor can people be both rhapsodes and actors.'

'True.'

'Nor even tragic actors and comic actors. All these things are b imitations, aren't they?'

'Yes.'

'Now it seems to me as if human nature is specialized even more minutely than this. It is unable to imitate many things well, or to do well the things of which the imitations are likenesses.'

'True.' [...]

397e 'But perhaps you would say it didn't suit our "republic", for we have no double or multiple men, because everybody performs one function. This is the only city where we shall find the cobbler a cobbler and not a ship's pilot as well, the farmer a farmer and not a juryman as well, and the man of war a man of war and not a man of money. Isn't it?'

'It is.'

398 'Suppose then there arrived in our city a man who could make himself into anything by his own skill, and could imitate everything. Suppose he brought his poems and wanted to give a display. We should salute him as divine, wonderful, a pleasure-giver: but we should then say that there is no one of his sort in our city and it is not allowed that there should be. We

should therefore pour ointment on his head, give him a garland of wool, and send him off elsewhere.'

From *Republic*, Book 10

'There are many respects in which I feel convinced, when I re-   595a
flect on it, that we founded our city rightly—and not least in the business of poetry.'

'In what way?'

'In our refusing to admit imitative poetry. It is even clearer, I think, that we ought not to admit it, now that we have distinguished the elements in the mind.'

'How so?'   b

'Between ourselves—and I know you're not going to denounce me to the writers of tragedy and all the other imitators—all this kind of thing is ruination to the listeners' minds, unless they are protected by the knowledge of what really is.'

'What are you thinking of?'

'I shall have to be frank—though my lifelong liking and respect for Homer inhibits me, for he is the prime teacher and   c
leader of all these fine folk. Still, persons mustn't be put before the truth. As I say, I shall have to be frank.'

'Indeed you will.'

'Listen then—or rather answer.'

'Ask away.'

'Can you tell me what imitation in general is? I can't see myself what it means.'

'Then it's hardly likely that I should.'

'There would be nothing surprising if you did. Duller eyes often see sooner than sharp ones.'   596

'I dare say. But with you there I shouldn't be able even to want to speak if I had an idea. *You* try and see.'

'Would you like us to begin with our usual procedure? We

9

are in the habit of assuming a "Form" in relation to each group of particular objects to which we apply the same name. Or do you not understand?'

'I understand.'

'Let us posit then any of the sets of many things you like. For
b instance, there are many beds and many tables.'

'Yes.'

'But there are only two Forms of these articles, one of bed and one of table.'

'Yes.'

'Now we are in the habit of saying that the manufacturer of these two articles looks to the Form and so makes either the beds or the tables we use, and similarly with everything else. None of the manufacturers makes the Form itself, surely?'

'Of course not.'

'Now see what you call the manufacturer I'm going to describe.'

c 'What manufacturer?'

'The one who makes all the things that each of the workmen makes.'

'That's a very marvellous person.'

'You'll say that even more in a moment. For this same workman is capable of making not only articles of furniture but everything that grows out of the earth and every animal, including himself, and indeed earth and heaven and gods and everything in heaven and in Hades beneath the earth. He makes it all.'

d 'That's a very clever professional you're talking about.'

'Don't you believe me? Tell me now, do you think that there can't be such a manufacturer, or that there might be a maker of all these things in some way? Don't you realize that you might yourself be able to make all these things in a way?'

'What way?'

'Not a difficult one, but contrived in many ways and quickly—quickest of all perhaps, if you will pick up a mirror and carry it
e round. You'll soon create the sun and the objects in the sky, and

the earth, and yourself and all the other animals and articles and plants and everything we were talking about.'

'Yes, but appearances, not the real things.'

'Well said, and to the point. The painter also is a craftsman of this sort, isn't he?'

'Yes, of course.'

'But you will say that what he makes isn't real, though in a way the painter also makes a bed.'

'Yes, the appearance of a bed.'

'But what about the bed-maker? Didn't you say just now that 597 he doesn't make the Form, which we call "what a bed is", but an individual bed?'

'I did.'

'So, if he doesn't make what is, he doesn't make the real thing, but something resembling it but distinct from it. And it might not be right if one said that the work of the bed-maker or any other workman was completely the real thing?'

'Well, no, at least in the view of people who are familiar with this sort of argument.'

'So let us not be surprised if this too is a dim object compared with reality.'

'Indeed not.' b

'Would you like us then, using these examples, to investigate this imitator, and see who he is?'

'If you like.'

'Well then, there are these three beds: one in nature, which we might say god makes—or is there someone else?'

'No, there isn't.'

'And one which the carpenter makes.'

'Yes.'

'And one which the painter makes.'

'Let us say so.'

'Painter, bed-maker, god—these three preside over three sorts of beds.'

'Yes.'

'Now god—whether he so chose or whether there was some c

necessity not to make more than one bed in nature—made just this one, which is what a bed is; two or more such beds never were produced by god nor will they ever be.'

'How so?'

'Because, if he made just two, there would be one other the Form of which both would possess, and this would be "what a bed is", not the two.'

'Right.'

d   'Well, god knew this, I imagine, and wanting to be the real maker of a real bed, not an individual maker of an individual bed, produced the one in nature.'

'Seems likely.'

'Then would you like us to call him its "nature-maker" or something like that?'

'That would be proper, seeing that he has made this and everything else in nature.'

'Then what about the carpenter? Is not he a manufacturer of a bed?'

'Yes.'

'Is the painter also a manufacturer and maker of such a thing?'

'Certainly not.'

'What would you say is his relationship to the bed?'

e   'I think the fairest thing would be to call him an imitator of that of which the others are manufacturers.'

'Very well. You call him an imitator in respect of the product third removed from nature.'

'That's right.'

'Then the tragic poet also, since he is an imitator, will be in the same position, third in order from king and truth, and so will all other imitators be.' […]

605c   'But we still haven't brought the greatest accusation against him. It is a terrible thought that he can ruin good men, apart from a very few.'

'But of course he can, if he does this.'

'Listen and think. When the best of us hear Homer or some other tragic poet imitating a hero in mourning, delivering a long speech of lamentation, singing or beating his breast, you d know how we feel pleasure and give ourselves up to it, how we follow in sympathy and praise the excellence of the poet who does this to us most effectively.'

'Of course I know.'

'But when we have some private bereavement, you notice how we pride ourselves on the opposite reaction—on keeping quiet and sticking it out—because this is a man's reaction, and the other, which we were praising just now, is a woman's.' e

'I notice that.'

'Is this approval proper? Is it right not to be disgusted, but to feel pleasure and give praise when you see a man who you would be ashamed to be yourself?'

'Well, it's not reasonable.'

'No, especially if you look at it like this.' 606

'Like what?'

'The element which is forcibly restrained in our own misfortunes, starved of tears and the satisfaction of lamentation, though it naturally desires this, is the very element which is satisfied and given pleasure by the poets. In these circumstances, our best element, not being adequately trained by reason or habituation, relaxes its watch over the element of b lamentation, because the sorrows it sees are others' sorrows and there seems no disgrace in praising and pitying a man who claims to be virtuous and is mourning out of season; indeed, the pleasure seems a positive gain, and we can't bear to reject the whole poem and be deprived of it. Not many people can see that the consequences of others' experiences invade one's own, because it is difficult to restrain pity in one's own misfortunes when it has grown strong on others.'

'Very true.' c

'Does not the same apply to the ridiculous? Suppose you enjoy in a comedy or a private conversation jokes you would be ashamed to make yourself, instead of disliking them as morally bad—aren't you doing the same thing as with the expressions of pity? You are releasing the element in you that likes jokes, and that you used to restrain by reason because you were afraid of a reputation for buffoonery. Without realizing it, you have made a big thing of it by your frequent indulgence in private conversation, with the result that you've become a comedian.'

'Quite so.'

d   'Poetical imitation in fact produces the same effect in regard to sex and anger and all the desires and pleasures and pains of the mind—and these, in our view, accompany every action. It waters them and nourishes them, when they ought to be dried up. It makes them our rulers, when they ought to be under control so that we can be better and happier people rather than worse and more miserable.'

'I cannot but agree.'

e   'So when you find admirers of Homer saying that he educated Greece and that for human management and education one ought to take him up and learn his lesson and direct one's whole life on his principles, you must be kind and polite to them— they are as good as they are able to be—and concede that
607 Homer is the foremost and most poetical of the tragic poets, but you must be clear in your mind that the only poetry admissible in our city is hymns to the gods and encomia to good men. If you accept the "sweetened Muse" in lyric or epic, pleasure and pain will be enthroned in your city instead of law and the principle which the community accepts as best in any given situation.'

'True.'

b   'Well, these were the points that I wanted to recall to complete our justification for wishing to banish poetry from the city, such being its nature. The argument forced us. But let us say to her, lest she damn us as coarse and philistine, that there is an old quarrel between poetry and philosophy: I could quote a lot of passages for that.'

ARISTOTLE

POETICS

representation
- necessary → learning
- natural → seperates us from the
  animals

I. THE VARIOUS KINDS OF POETRY

Introduction

1. What is poetry, how many kinds of it are there, and what are 1447a
their specific effects? That is our topic, and we will inquire how
stories are to be put together to make a good poetical work, and
what is the number and nature of poetry's component parts, 10
and raise other questions arising in the same area of inquiry. We
shall make our start, as is natural, from first principles.

Poetry as a species of representation

Epic poetry and tragedy, as well as comedy and dithyramb,*
and most music for flute and lyre are all, taken as a whole, forms 15
of representation. They differ from each other in three ways,
either in respect of the medium, the object, or the mode of
their representation.

Differences of medium

People represent and portray objects by using colours and
shapes to make visible images of them; some do this by skill,
and others by practice. Others again make use of the voice. 20
In like manner, all the literary genres mentioned make use of
rhythm, language, and melody, whether separately or in combination. Music for flute and lyre and other instruments with
similar effects, such as pipes, make use of melody and rhythm 25
only. Dancers make use of rhythm alone: it is by rhythm expressed in bodily movement that they mime character, emotion,
and action. There is an art that uses language unaccompanied,
whether prose or verse, sometimes in a single metre and sometimes in combination: this so far remains unnamed. For there 1447b
is no common name for us to give to the skits of Sophron and

10 Xenarchus* on the one hand and to the Socratic dialogues* on the other. Nor is there one for any other representation that one might produce in iambic trimeters or elegiac couplets or any other metre.* To be sure, people attach the name 'poetry' to the verse-form, and speak of elegiac poets and epic poets. But this classification has no regard to the representative aspect of their
15 poetry but only to the metre they share, so that writers are so described even if they publish medical or scientific treatises in metrical form. In fact Homer and Empedocles* have nothing in common except their metre; the former can be called a poet, but the latter should be termed a scientist. On the other hand,
20 if someone were to compose in the greatest possible variety of metres—as Chaeremon did in his *Centaur*, a rhapsody containing every single metre—he would still deserve to be called a poet. That is how we should classify in this area. There are also arts that make use of all the media we have mentioned—
25 rhythm, melody, and metre. Examples are dithyramb, nomes,* tragedy, and comedy. They differ in that the first two make use of them all together, and the last two in specific parts. These different ways in which the arts effect representation are what I call differences of medium.

Differences of objects

1448a 2. The things that representative artists represent are the actions of people, and if people are represented they are necessarily either superior or inferior, better or worse, than we are. (Differences in character you see derive from these categories, since it is by virtue or vice that people are ethically distinct from
5 each other.) So too with painters: Polygnotus* portrayed better people, Pauson worse people, and Dionysius people just like us. Clearly, each of the kinds of representation so far mentioned will exhibit these differences, and will differ from the others by representing objects that are distinct in this way. These dissimilarities can occur even in ballet and in music for flute and lyre,
10 no less than in prose and unaccompanied verse. For instance,

18

Homer represents people better than us and Cleophon people similar to us, while people worse than us figure in the works of Hegemon of Thasos, the inventor of parodies, and Nicochares who wrote the *Deiliad*.* The same is the case with dithyrambs and nomes: one could represent Cyclopses in the manner of Timotheus and Philoxenus.* The very same difference makes 15 the distinction between tragedy and comedy: the latter aims to represent people as worse, and the former as better, than people nowadays are.

Differences in mode

3. A third difference is in the mode of representation of each of these objects. Within the same medium it is possible to repre- 20 sent the same objects either by narrative or by dramatization. Narrative may be borne throughout by a single narrator, or with variation as in Homer. In dramatization all the personages play their parts as active agents.

So representation, as we said initially, can be differentiated in these three respects: medium, object, and mode. So, in respect 25 of representation, Sophocles belongs in one way with Homer, since they both represent superior people, but in another way with Aristophanes, since they both represent people in dramatic activity. This is why, according to some people, drama got its name—for the word is derived from a Greek verb for doing, namely *dran*. This too is why the Dorians* claim owner- 30 ship of both tragedy and comedy, offering the names as evidence. Comedy is claimed by the Megarians—both those on the mainland who date it to the time of their democracy, and those in Sicily which was the birthplace of the poet Epicharmus, who lived long before Chionides and Magnes.* Tragedy is claimed by some inhabitants of the Peloponnese. The Dorians 35 point out that they call villages *komai* while the Athenians call them *demoi*; the assumption is that comedians got their name not because the Greek word for revelry is *komazein*, but because they strolled through villages having been ejected in

disgrace from the city. Again the Dorians say that their word
1448b for doing is *dran*, while the Athenians say *prattein*.

So much, then, for the number of ways in which representation can be classified, and what they are.

The origins of poetry and its early development

4. Two things, both of them natural, seem likely to have been
5 the causes of the origin of poetry. Representation comes naturally to human beings from childhood,* and so does the universal pleasure in representations. Indeed, this marks off humans from other animals: man is prone to representation beyond all others, and learns his earliest lessons through representation. A common phenomenon is evidence of this: even when things are
10 painful to look upon—corpses, for instance, or the shapes of the most revolting animals—we take pleasure in viewing highly realistic images of them. The further explanation of this is that learning is delightful not only to philosophers but to ordinary people as well, even though they have less capacity for it. That
15 is why people like seeing images, because as they look at them they understand and work out what each item is, for example, 'this is so-and-so'.* Whereas, if one is unacquainted with the subject, one's pleasure will not be in the representation, but in the technique or the colour or some other element.

20   Representation, then, comes naturally to us, as do melody and rhythm (which obviously includes metre as a sub-class); and so it was that, from the beginning, those with the greatest natural gift for such things by a gradual process of improvement developed poetry out of improvisation.

This, however, took two different forms according to the
25 characters of the authors: the more serious among them represented noble people and noble actions, and the more frivolous represented the actions of ignoble people. The latter began by composing invectives, while the former produced hymns and panegyrics. We cannot identify a poem of that kind by any poet earlier than Homer, though there are likely to have been many

such; but from Homer onwards we can do so, beginning with   30
his own *Margites* and similar poems.* Because of its suitability
the iambic metre came into use in these poems, and the reason
why it is now called 'iambic' is because *iambizein* is the Greek
word for 'lampoon'. So some of the ancient poets composed
heroic epics and others iambic lampoons. Just as Homer was
the greatest poet in the serious style, unsurpassed not only in
composition but also in the dramatic power of his representation, so too he was the first to put comedy into shape for us,   35
no mere invective, but a dramatization of the ridiculous rather.
Thus his *Margites* stands in the same relation to our comedies
as the *Iliad* and the *Odyssey* do to our tragedies. Once tragedy   1449a
and comedy had made their appearance those who had an inclination towards either kind of poetry followed their natural
bent and either composed comedies in place of lampoons or
composed tragedies in place of epics. This was because these   5
new art forms were grander and more highly esteemed than
the old.

Tragedy

This is not the place to inquire whether even now tragedy is all
that it should be in respect of its constituent elements, whether
in itself or in relation to its audiences. Certainly it originally
took shape out of improvisations. (This is true of tragedy as
well as of comedy: the former began with the leaders of the   10
dithyramb, and the latter from the leaders of the phallic singing* that is a tradition that still survives in many cities.) Then
it developed gradually as people exploited new possibilities as
they came to light. After undergoing many changes tragedy
ceased to evolve, having achieved its natural condition.   15

The number of actors was first increased from one to two
by Aeschylus, who also reduced the choral element and gave
primacy to the spoken word. The third actor and the practice of
scene-painting were introduced by Sophocles. Length was also
a factor. Tragedy acquired its dignity only at a late stage, when,

20 after a satyric period of short stories and comic diction, it
adopted the iambic trimeter instead of the trochaic tetrameter.
Tetrameter had been used at first as suitable to satyric verse and
easy to dance to, but when the spoken word prevailed nature
itself found the appropriate metre, because the iambic trimeter
25 is the metre closest to speech. Evidence of this is the fact that
we very often use iambics in conversation, while we utter hexameters very rarely and only when departing from our normal
tone. Another change took place in the number of episodes. Let
30 us take as read a number of further embellishments: it would no
doubt be laborious to discuss them individually.

Comedy

5. Comedy is, as we said, representation of people who are inferior but not wholly vicious: the ridiculous is one category of
the embarrassing. What is ridiculous is some error or embarrass-
35 ment that is neither painful nor life-threatening; for example, a
comic mask is ugly and distorted but does not cause pain. The
stages in the development of tragedy, and those responsible for
them, have stayed in people's memory; but the early history of
1449b comedy is unknown because no serious interest was taken in it.
It was only relatively recently that a magistrate* made provision
for a comic chorus; before that performers were volunteers.
The first mention of people called comic poets dates from a
time when comedy had already taken shape. It is not known
who introduced masks, prologues, multiple actors, and the like.
5 Comic stories, however, originated in Sicily; among Athenians,
it was Crates* who first abandoned the iambic style and began
to compose stories and plots of a general kind.

Epic

10 Epic poetry resembles tragedy in so far as it is a representation
in verse of superior subjects; but the two differ in that epic uses
only a single metre and is in narrative mode. They differ also in

length: tragedy tries so far as possible to keep within a period of twenty-four hours or thereabouts, while epic, in contrast, is unrestricted in time. (Initially, however, in this respect no dis- 15 tinction was made between tragedy and epic.) Epic and tragedy have some elements in common, while others are peculiar to tragedy. Hence, anyone who can tell what is good and what is bad in tragedy understands epic too, since all the elements of epic are present in tragedy even though not all the elements of tragedy are present in epic. 20

Leaving aside representation in hexameters and comedy for later discussion, let us now treat of tragedy, gathering up from what has already been said a definition of its essence.

II. THE NATURE OF TRAGEDY

Definition

6. Tragedy is a representation of an action of a superior kind— grand, and complete in itself—presented in embellished lan- 25 guage, in distinct forms in different parts, performed by actors rather than told by a narrator, effecting, through pity and fear, the purification* of such emotions.

By 'embellished language' I mean language with rhythm and melody. When I say 'in distinct forms in different parts' I mean that some parts are in unaccompanied verse while others have 30 melody as an extra.

Since the representation is performed by actors, a neces- sary part of tragedy must be the presentation on stage of the performance. In addition there is music-making and there is style, for these are the media of their representation. By 'style' I mean simply the composition of the verse; the meaning of 'music-making' is obvious to everyone.* 35

Now tragedy is the repesentation of action, and action involves

agents who will necessarily have certain qualities of both character and intellect. It is because of the qualities of the agents that we
1450a classify their actions, and it is because of their actions that they
succeed or fail in life. It is the story of the action that is the rep-
5 resentation. By the 'story' I mean the plot of the events. 'Moral
character' is what makes us evaluate agents in particular ways,
while 'ideas' are what is expressed in the speeches used to prove
a case or enunciate a truth.

Basic elements of tragedy

Hence, tragedy as a whole necessarily has six elements on the
basis of which it is evaluated, namely, the story, the moral elem-
10 ent, the style, the ideas, the staging, and the music. Two of these
elements concern the means, one concerns the mode, and three
concern the objects of the mimesis; and there is nothing else
besides. Not a few tragedians can be said to have made use of
these items, since every drama alike involves staging, a moral
element, and a story, plus style and music and intellectual
content.

The primacy of plot

15 The most important element is the construction of the plot.
Tragedy is a representation not of persons but of action and
life, and happiness and unhappiness consist in action. The
point is action, not character: it is their moral status that gives
people the character they have, but it is their actions that make
20 them happy or unhappy. So it is not in order to portray moral
character that the actors perform; rather, they include character for the sake of action. The events, the story, are the point of
tragedy, and that is the most important thing of all.

Again, there could not be a tragedy without action, but there
could be one without moral character—indeed, the tragedies
25 of most modern poets completely lack the moral element, and
in general there are many such poets. Compare, in painting,

the relationship between Zeuxis and Polygnotus: Polygnotus is a good portrayer of character, while Zeuxis' painting is totally lacking in it.* Further, if someone sets out a series of speeches expressive of moral character, polished in style and rich in ideas, it will not achieve the effect of tragedy. A tragedy deficient in these elements, provided that it has a story and a structured plot, will do so much more effectively. Moreover, the most important devices that tragedy uses to affect the emotions are parts of the story—namely, reversals and discoveries. One other indication is that novice poets can master style and moral character before they can compose plots—the same goes for almost all the early poets.

So the story is the foundation and as it were the soul of tragedy, while moral character is secondary. (The like holds in painting: if someone were to apply the most beautiful colours to a surface at random, he would give less pleasure than if he had sketched a portrait in black and white.) Tragedy is representation of action, and it is chiefly for the sake of action that it represents people in action.

Third come the ideas, that is, the power of expressing what is involved in or appropriate to a situation—something that, in prose, is the function of the arts of statesmanship and rhetoric. Earlier poets made people speak like statesmen; contemporary poets make them speak like orators. Moral character is what reveals the nature of people's fundamental options; that is why there is no such thing in speeches in which the speaker reveals no choice or rejection. Intelligence, on the other hand, is expressed in what people say to show that something is or is not a fact, or to support some universal proposition.

The fourth element is style. By 'style', as I said, is meant the expression of thought in words, an effect that can be produced either in prose or in verse.

Of the remaining elements, music is the most important source of pleasure. Staging can be emotionally attractive, but is not a matter of art and is not integral to poetry. The power of tragedy can be exercised without actors and without

30

35

1450b

5

10

15

25

20 a performance. Staging belongs more to the scene-painter's art than to that of the poets.

Characteristics of a good plot

7. Given these definitions, let us next discuss the proper construction of the plot, since this is the first and most important element in tragedy.

COMPLETENESS

We have laid it down that tragedy is a representation of an action that is whole and entire and on an appropriate scale.
25 (A thing may be a whole and yet be wanting in scale.) A whole is something that has a beginning, a middle, and an end. A beginning is an item that does not itself follow necessarily upon something else, but which has some second item following necessarily upon it. Conversely, an end is an item that
30 naturally follows, either necessarily or commonly, upon something else, but has nothing following it. A middle is an item that both follows upon a preceding item and has another item following upon itself. Stories that are well constructed should not begin at some arbitrary point but should conform to the stated pattern.

SCALE

Moreover, any beautiful object, whether a living organism or
35 any other thing made up of parts, must have those parts not only in proper order but also on an appropriate scale. Beauty consists in scale as well as order, which is why there could not be a beautiful organism that was either minuscule or gigantic. In the first case, a glimpse that is so brief as to be close to vanishing-point cannot be distinct. In the second case—say, of an animal a thousand miles long—the impossibility of taking all in
1451a at a single glance means that unity and wholeness is lost to the viewer. So, just as physical bodies and living organisms need to be on an appropriate scale that allows them to be taken in by the

eye, likewise stories should have an appropriate length, which is
such as to enable them to be held in memory.   5

A limit of length determined by the rules of competitions
and the capacity of audiences does not feature in the art of
poetry. If you had to arrange a competition for a hundred
tragedies you would time them by water-clocks. (On one occasion this is actually said to have taken place.)* The limit that   10
is set by the nature of the subject is this: the longer the story,
the grander the scale, provided it remains comprehensible as a
whole. To give a general formula: an adequate limit of length is
a size that permits a transformation from adversity to prosperity, or from prosperity to adversity, in a probable or necessary   15
sequence of events.

UNITY

8. A story that is built around a single person is not, as some
people think, thereby unified. An infinity of things happen to a
single individual, not all of which constitute a unity; likewise,
a single person performs many actions which do not add up to
make a single action. So all those poets who compose a Hera-   20
cleid or a Thesiad have clearly got things wrong, assuming that
just because Heracles was one person his story too is sure to
have a unity. Homer, here as elsewhere surpassing all others,
grasped this point firmly, whether by art or instinct. When he
composed the *Odyssey* he did not include just everything that   25
happened to Odysseus, such as getting wounded on Parnassus,
or pretending to be mad to avoid conscription, for these events
had no necessary or probable connection with each other. Instead he constructed the *Odyssey*, and the *Iliad* too, around a
single action of the kind we have been discussing.   30

In other representative arts a single representation has
a single object. In just the same way a story, since it is the
representation of an action, should concern an action that
is single and entire, with its several incidents so structured
that the displacement or removal of any one of them would
disturb and dislocate the whole. If the presence or absence of

something makes no discernible difference, then it is no part of
35 the whole.

UNIVERSALITY AND NECESSITY

9. From what has been said it is clear that the poet's job is not
relating what actually happened, but rather the kind of thing
that *would* happen—that is to say, what is possible in terms of
probability and necessity. The difference between a historian
1451b and a poet is not a matter of using verse or prose: you might put
the works of Herodotus into verse and it would be a history in
verse no less than in prose. The difference is that the one relates
what actually happened, and the other the kinds of events that
would happen.

5   For this reason poetry is more philosophical and more serious
than history; poetry utters universal truths, history particular
statements. The universal truths concern what befits a person of
a certain kind to say or do in accordance with probability and
necessity—and that is the aim of poetry, even if it makes use of
10 proper names.* A particular statement tells us what (for example)
Alcibiades* did or what happened to him. In the case of comedy
this is already manifest: the poets make up the story on the basis
of probability and then attach names to the characters at random;
they do not write about particular individuals as the lampoon-
15 ists used to do. In the case of tragedy they retain the traditional
names. The reason for this is that what is possible is credible. If
something has not happened we are inclined to disbelieve that it
is possible; but it is obvious that what has happened is possible,
since if it were not it would never have happened. Nevertheless,
even among tragedies there are some where only one or two of
20 the names are familiar, while the rest are made up; and there are
some plays without a single familiar name, for instance Agathon's
*Antheus.** In that play both the events and the names are inven-
tions, but it gives no less pleasure on that account. So there is no
need to adhere at all costs to the traditional stories of tragedy.
25 Indeed, it would be absurd to try, since even what is familiar is
familiar only to a few, and yet it gives pleasure to everyone.

It is clear from all this that the poet must be a maker of stories rather than verses, in so far as it is representation that makes him a poet, and representation is of actions. Even if it turns out that he is writing about historical events he is no less a poet 30 for that, since nothing prevents such events being the kind of thing that would happen. It is in that respect that he deals with them as a poet.

Of defective stories* and actions, the worst are those that are episodic. I call a story episodic when the sequence of episodes is neither necessary nor probable. Bad poets compose stories of 35 this kind of their own accord, but even good ones do so under pressure from the actors. Writing pieces for competitions, they drag out the story and are often forced to distort the sequence of events.

Tragedy is an imitation not just of a complete action, but 1452a of events that evoke pity and fear.* These effects occur above all when things come about unexpectedly but at the same time consequentially. This will produce greater astonishment than if they come about spontaneously or by chance—for even chance 5 events are found more astonishing when they seemed to have happened for a purpose. Think of the time in Argos when Mitys' murderer was killed by Mitys' statue falling onto him as he was looking up at it! Such things are not thought to occur randomly. So inevitably, stories of this kind will be better. 10

Types and elements of plot

10. Stories can be classified as simple or complex, since the actions of which they are the representations are similarly classified in the first instance. I call an action simple if it is, in the sense defined, continuous and unitary, and in which the change of fortune takes place without reversal or discovery; I call it 15 complex if the change of fortune involves a reversal or a discovery or both.* These should grow naturally out of the plot of the story, so that they come about, with necessity or probability, from the preceding events. There is a great difference between 20

29

something happening *after* certain events and happening *because of* those events.

Reversal and discovery

11. Reversal is a change of direction in the course of events, as already stated, taking place, as we insist, in accord with probability or necessity. For instance, in *Oedipus* a messenger comes
25 to bring Oedipus good news and rid him of his fears about his mother; but by revealing his true identity he produces the opposite effect.* Again, in the *Lynceus* the hero is being led off to death, with Danaus* behind him as executioner, yet the upshot of events earlier in the story is that Danaus dies and the hero survives.

30 Discovery, as the term implies, is a change from ignorance to knowledge, and thus to either love or hate, on the part of those destined for good or bad fortune. Discovery takes its finest form when it coincides with reversal, as in the *Oedipus*. There are, of course, other kinds of discovery, for what has been de-
35 scribed can occur in reference to inanimate and chance objects; and there is also such a thing as discovering whether someone has or has not done something. But the one that has most to do with the story and most to do with the action is the one described. Reversal and discovery together will evoke either pity
1452b or fear—just the kind of actions of which, according to our basic principle, tragedy offers an imitation—and will serve to bring about the happy or unhappy ending.

Since detection is something that takes place between people, it may be either the detection of one person by another
5 (whose own identity is clear) or mutual recognition between a pair (for example, Iphigeneia was recognized by Orestes when she sent the letter, but something different was needed for her to recognize Orestes).*

These, then, are two components of the story: reversal
10 and discovery; a third component is suffering, which is an action involving pain or destruction, such as murders on stage,

extreme agony, woundings, and so on. The other two elements
have already been explained.

The sequence of scenes in tragedy

12. The parts of tragedy that should be considered as its formal elements were mentioned earlier. In sequential terms the   15
separate sections into which it is divided are the following: prologue, episode, finale, and chorus parts (sung either on entry or
while stationary). These items are common to all plays; some
have in addition arias and dirges.

A prologue is everything in a tragedy that precedes the opening chorus; an episode is whatever comes between two com-   20
plete choral songs; and the finale is everything that comes after
the final chorus. Of the choral part, the opening chorus is the
first complete utterance of the chorus; while a stationary ode is
a choral song without anapaests or trochees. A dirge is a lament
shared between the chorus and the actors.

We have already mentioned the parts of tragedy that should   25
be regarded as its formal elements; the ones just mentioned are
the separate sections in sequential terms.

III. EXCELLENCE IN TRAGEDY

13. What should one aim at, and what should one avoid, when
putting together a story? What will enable tragedy to achieve its
effect? This is the next topic after what has been said.   30

Guidelines for plot construction

For tragedy at its best the plot should be complex, not simple,
and it should be representative of fearsome and pitiable events,
for that is the specific feature of this kind of representation.
Hence it is clear first of all that good men should not be shown

35 passing from good fortune to bad, for that evokes not fear or
pity, but outrage. Nor should depraved men be shown passing from bad fortune to good—this indeed is the least tragic
of all: it has none of the appropriate features, evoking neither
1453a pity nor fear nor even basic human sympathy. Finally, a very
wicked man should not be shown passing from good fortune
to bad: this may evoke basic human sympathy, but neither pity
nor fear. One of those sentiments, namely pity, has to do with
5 undeserved misfortune, and the other, namely fear, has to do
with someone who is like ourselves. Accordingly, there will be
nothing in the outcome to evoke either pity or fear.

We are left, then, with the person in between: a man not
outstanding in virtue or justice, brought down through vice
or depravity, who falls into adversity not through vice or
10 depravity but because he errs in some way.* He is a personage
enjoying renown and prosperity, such as Oedipus, Thyestes,*
and eminent persons from families of that kind. A well-made
story, then, will have a single rather than (as some argue) a
double upshot, and it will involve a change not from bad fortune to good, but from good fortune to bad. The cause of the
15 change will not be depravity, but a serious error on the part
of a character such as we have described (or someone better
rather than worse). Evidence of this is provided by history. At
first poets picked out stories at random, but nowadays the best
tragedies are always constructed around a few families, for ex-
20 ample, about Alcmaeon, Oedipus, Orestes, Meleager, Thyestes,
Telephus,* and any others whose lot has been to do or suffer
something terrible.

Accordingly, the best tragedy, technically, follows this plot.
Critics who find fault with Euripides for doing this in his tragedies, most of which have an unhappy ending, are making the
25 mistake that I mentioned earlier. For this, as has been said, is
the right thing to do. The best evidence for this is the fact that
on the stage, and in competitions, such plays, if well performed,
are the most tragic. Euripides, even if he mismanages some
other matters, is at all events the most tragic of the poets.

Second best is the kind of plot which some people like most: 30
a double plot like the *Odyssey*, with a different ending for the
better and worse characters. It is regarded as best only because
of the weaknesses of the audience; the poets follow the lead of
their public and pander to its taste. But this is not the pleasure proper to tragedy, but is more characteristic of comedy. 35
In comedy even those who are bitter enemies in the story, like
Orestes and Aegisthus,* make friends and go off together at the
end, and nobody gets killed by anybody.

The source of the tragic effect

14. Actually seeing a play performed may evoke fear and pity, 1453a
but so too can the plot itself—this is more fundamental and
the mark of a better poet. The story should be put together in
such a way that even without seeing the play a person hearing
the series of events should feel dread and pity. This is what 5
someone would feel on hearing the story of Oedipus. Evoking this effect by a stage performance is less artistic and more
dependent on the production. The effect that some producers
try to achieve is not so much fear as horror: that has nothing at
all to do with tragedy. One should not look to it for every kind 10
of enjoyment, but only the appropriate one. The poet's job is to
use representation to make us enjoy the tragic emotions of pity
and fear, and this has to be built into his plots.

Let us therefore ask what kinds of event strike us as terrible or pitiable. The interactions in question must necessarily 15
occur either between friends and relations, or between enemies,
or strangers. If an enemy takes on an enemy, there is nothing
in his acting or planning to arouse pity, only the actual suffering of the victim. So too when the characters are strangers.
What should be looked for are cases where the sufferings occur
within relationships, as between brother and brother, son and 20
father, mother and son, son and mother—where one kills, or
is on the point of killing, the other, or is doing something else
horrible.

The traditional stories should not be tampered with—Clytemnestra must be killed by Orestes, and Eriphyle by Alcmaeon, and so on—but the poet needs to be inventive and
25 make the best use of the traditional material. Let me explain what I mean by 'the best use'. The deed may be perpetrated in full knowledge and awareness, which is the way the old poets showed things, and as Euripides too made Medea kill her
30 children.* It is also possible for the terrible deed to be done in ignorance, and the relationship be discovered only later, as with Sophocles' Oedipus. Here the deed is outside the play; examples within the tragedy itself are Astydamas' *Alcmaeon* or Telegonus in the *Odysseus Wounded*. A third possibility in ad-
35 dition to these two is when a person is on the point of unwittingly doing some irreparable deed, but realizes the situation in time to desist. There is no further possibility, since the deed is either done or not done, and the agents must either know or not know.

Of these, the worst is being on the point of doing the deed knowingly, and then not doing it. This is monstrous without being tragic, since no one suffers. That is why poets never, or
1454a only very rarely, compose in this way (one example is Haemon and Creon in *Antigone*).* Second worst is the actual performance of the deed. This is best if the deed is one that is done in ignorance, with the relationship discovered only later—here there is nothing monstrous, and the discovery will make a great impression. Best of all is the last case: I mean, for example,
5 when in *Cresphontes* Merope is on the point of killing her son, and recognizes him in time.* The same happens with sister and brother in the *Iphigeneia*, and in *Helle* when the son recognizes his mother when about to hand her over to the enemy.*

This is why, as I said earlier, not many families provide ma-
10 terial for tragedy. It was chance, not art, that guided poets in their search for stories in which to produce their effects, so they are obliged to turn to the families who have suffered such woes.

Enough has now been said about the construction of plots
15 and the kinds of stories that are appropriate.

34

Character in tragedy

15. We turn to moral character.* Here there are four things to aim at. The first and foremost is that the characters should be good.* As was said earlier, moral character will be shown if a speech or action reveals the nature of a person's fundamental choice,* and the character will be good if the choice is good. This is possible in every class of person: there is such a thing as a good woman and a good slave, even if one of these is perhaps 20 inferior, and the other base. The second point is appropriateness: it is no good for a character to be courageous if the courage or intelligence is expressed in a way that is not appropriate for a woman. The third aim is plausibility, which is something different from making the character good and appropriate in 25 the manner described. The fourth item is consistency: even if the character portrayed is someone inconsistent, and that is the whole point of the representation, he should nevertheless be consistently inconsistent.

An example of unnecessary badness of character is Menelaus in *Orestes*,* of inapt and inappropriate character the dirge 30 of Odysseus in *Scylla* and the speech of Melanippe;* of inconsistency in the *Iphigeneia in Aulis*—the girl who pleads to be spared is not at all like her later self.* In the case of moral character no less than in plot, we should always look for what is necessary or probable: it should be necessary or probable for this kind of person to say or do this kind of thing, and it should 35 be necessary or probable for one kind of event to follow another kind of event.

Clearly, the explication* of a story should issue from the story itself, and not from a *deus ex machina* as in the *Medea*,* or in the 1454b departure scene in the *Iliad*.* A *deus ex machina* may be used for events outside the play—for past events beyond human ken, or subsequent events that can only be described in prophecy— since we believe that the gods are all-seeing. But there should 5 not be anything implausible in the events themselves; or if there is, it should be outside the play, as with Sophocles' *Oedipus*.

Since tragedy is a representation of people who are better
10 than we are, poets should copy good portrait-painters, who
portray a person's features and offer a good likeness but none-
theless make him look handsomer than he is. In the same way,
a poet exhibiting people who are irascible and indolent should
show them as they are, and yet portray them as good men—in
the way that Homer made Achilles both a good man and a para-
15 digm of stubbornness.*

These points are to be kept in mind throughout, and also
the features of stage production that are essential to the art of
poetry. Many mistakes are possible in this area. But they have
been discussed in detail in my published works.

Further thoughts on discovery

16. Discovery has already been explained. It comes in six
kinds.
20 The first is identification by signs and tokens—this is the
least artistic form, though because of writers' lack of ingenuity
it is the one most used. Some of these are congenital marks, like
'the spear the earth-born bear' or stars like the ones Carcinus
uses in *Thyestes*, while others are acquired. Marks of this second kind may be bodily, such as scars, or external tokens, such
25 as necklaces or the boat that leads to the discovery in *Tyro*.*
Even these can be put to better or worse use: the way in which
Odysseus' scar leads to his recognition by his nurse is different
from the way in which it leads to his recognition by the swineherds. Recognitions that are merely to add plausibility—and all
others of a similar kind—are less artistic; far superior are those
linked to the reversal, as in the bath scene.*
30 Second are identifications that are made by the poet himself, which for that reason are inartistic. For example: Orestes
in *Iphigeneia* reveals his own identity. Iphigeneia's identity is
revealed by the letter, whereas Orestes is made to say in his own
person what the poet, and not the story, demands. This makes
35 it close to the error just discussed: he might well have brought

some tokens with him. Another case is 'the voice of the shuttle' in Sophocles' *Tereus*.*

Third there is identification through memory, when the matter is brought to mind by something seen or heard. A case in point is Dicaiogenes' *Cyprians*, where the hero bursts into 1455a tears at the sight of the painting; another is the moment when Odysseus, telling his tale to Alcinous, weeps at the memories brought back by the sound of the harp. In each case recognition ensues.

Fourth there is identification by inference. The *Choephorae* provides an example: 'Someone resembling me has come; no one resembles me except Orestes; therefore Orestes has come.'* 5 Polyides the Sophist suggested another in connection with *Iphigeneia*; he said it was natural for Orestes to infer: 'My sister was sacrificed, and so I will be too.' Another case is in Theodectes' *Tydeus*: 'I came to find a son, so I am doomed myself.' Again, in *Phinaedae*, when the women see the place: 'This is 10 where we were exposed, so this is where we are to die.'

There is also a complicated kind of identification based on fallacious reasoning by the audience. For instance, in *Odysseus the False Messenger*: the premise that the poet offers is that Odysseus, and he alone, can bend the bow. Odysseus himself says that he will recognize the bow which he had never seen. The identification actually takes place on the former basis, when the audience thinks fallaciously that it takes place on the latter.* 15

The best discovery of all is one that ensues from the actual course of events, where the emotional impact is achieved through a probable sequence, as in Sophocles' *Oedipus* and in *Iphigeneia* (her desire to send a letter is entirely probable). Only this kind of identification can make do without artificial marks and necklaces. Second best are those that involve inference. 20

Advice to playwrights

17. When plotting stories and putting them into words one should do one's best to visualize the events. By envisaging

37

things while they happen, as if one were an eyewitness, one will
25 discover what is appropriate and one will be less likely to over-
look inconsistencies. Evidence of this is offered by the criticism
that was made of Carcinus. At the crucial moment Amphiaraus
was returning from the temple—this would not be noticed by
someone who did not see it, but on the stage it irritated the
audience and the play was a failure.

As far as possible, the poet should act the story as he writes
30 it. People of the same temperament are more persuasive if they
actually feel the emotions they enact: someone actually in distress best acts out distress, someone really angry best acts out
rage. This is why, in order to write tragic poetry, you must be
either a genius who can adapt himself to anything, or a madman
who lets himself get carried away.

1455b   The poet should first lay out the general structure and only
then elaborate it into episodes: this is true whether the story is
a ready-made one or a fresh composition. As an example
of what I call laying out the general structure, take *Iphigeneia*.
'A girl has been sacrificed and then vanishes without trace.
Unbeknownst to her sacrificers she is set down in another
5 country where it is the custom to sacrifice strangers to the
local goddess. She becomes the priestess of this rite. Much later
her brother happens to arrive, and on arrival is taken prisoner.
(His being sent by an oracle, and for what purpose, does not
belong to the story.) On the point of being sacrificed, he dis-
closes his identity—either as Euripides makes him do, or as
10 Polyidus suggested, by saying, not improbably: 'As my sister
was sacrificed, so must I be too'—and so he is saved. After that,
names are to be supplied and episodes worked out—but the
episodes should be appropriate, as are the fit of madness that
led to Orestes' arrest and the purification that led to his being
saved.

15   In plays the episodes are short; in epic they lengthen out the
poem. A summary of the *Odyssey* is not at all long. 'A man is
away from home for many years; he is kept under surveillance by
Poseidon and isolated. Meanwhile affairs at home are in such a

state that his property is being squandered by his wife's suitors, who are plotting against his son. After being shipwrecked he returns home, identifies himself to several people, and launches an attack in which his enemies are destroyed and he survives.' That is the core of the story; the rest is episodes.

18. Every tragedy has both a complication and an explication. What goes before the opening, and often some of the events inside the play, make up the complication; the rest is the explication. What I call complication is everything from the beginning up to the point that immediately precedes the change to good or bad fortune; everything from the beginning of the change to the end I call explication. Thus, in Theodectes' *Lynceus* the complication includes events before the play, the kidnapping of the child, and the [...] of the parents; the explication is everything from the accusation of murder until the end.*

Different kinds of tragedy

There are four kinds of tragedy—the same number as that of the component parts mentioned. There is the complex kind, constituted by reversal and discovery (for example, plays about Ajax or Ixion); there is the morality tragedy (for example, *Women of Phthia* and *Peleus*); finally there is [...] (e.g. *Daughters of Phorcys*, *Prometheus*, and plays set in the underworld).*

Preferably one should try to have all four, but if not all then the most important and as many as possible, especially given the way people criticize poets these days. Because in the past there have been good poets in each genre, people expect a present-day poet to surpass each of them in his own particular excellence.

If we are to compare and contrast tragedies, we must do so principally in respect of the story, that is, whether they share the same complication and explication. Many poets complicate well but explicate badly, but the two need to be matched to each other.

39

Final advice on plot construction

You must call to mind what I have said several times: one should never build a tragedy with an epic structure, that is to say, one containing more than one story. Suppose one were to make the entire story of the *Iliad* into one play! Epic is long enough for every episode to appear on an appropriate scale, but in a drama
15 the result is very disappointing. There is evidence of this. Consider those who have treated the sack of Troy as a whole, like Euripides, rather than piecemeal, or the whole story of Niobe, rather than what Aeschylus did. These people's plays were either complete failures or fared badly in the competition. There was even a play of Agathon's which was a flop simply because of this.

In reversals and in simple plots poets like to astonish us, in
20 order to produce a desired effect that is both tragic and humane. This happens when someone who is both clever and wicked (like Sisyphus*) is taken in, or when someone who is brave but unjust is worsted. This is not improbable, since, as Agathon remarks, it is probable that many improbable things should happen.

25 The chorus should be treated as one of the actors; it should be part of the whole and should take part in the action. Sophocles, not Euripides, should be the model here. With other poets the songs have no more to do with the story than with any other tragedy. That is why they sing interludes—a practice
30 commenced by Agathon. But what difference is there between singing interludes and transferring a speech or an episode from one play into another?

Style and intellectual content

19. Now that the other elements have been discussed it is time to speak about style and ideas. The topic of ideas, however,
35 can be left for my *Rhetoric*, the subject to which it more properly belongs. Under the head of ideas come all the effects that can be produced by reason: proof, refutation, the evocation of

emotions (pity, fear, anger, and so on) and also the placing or 1456b
removal of an emphasis. The same principles should be applied
to the management of events, when there is a need to represent
something as pitiful, or frightening, or important, or probable.
The difference is that in stage-management the effect is to be
produced without explicit statement, while in speeches the ef- 5
fect must be produced by the words of the speaker. What, indeed, would there be for the speaker to do if the required effects
were evident without anything being said?

One topic of inquiry, under the head of style, is the distinction between different speech acts: command, prayer, statement,
threat, question, answer, and so on. Knowledge of these is part 10
of the art of performance and of stage-direction: no serious
criticism of a poet can be made on the basis of his knowledge or
ignorance of such matters. Protagoras* complained that when 15
Homer writes, 'Sing, goddess, of the wrath . . .', he purports
to be uttering a prayer, but in fact he is giving an order, since
that is what telling somebody what to do or not to do actually is.
Why should anyone think that is a fault in Homer? So let us set
that aside as belonging to some art other than that of poetry.

Basic concepts of linguistics

20. Different grammatical elements go to make up style: phon- 20
eme, syllable, particle, noun, verb, conjunction, inflection, sentence. A phoneme is an indivisible vocal sound of a particular
kind: it must be able to form part of a composite vocal sound,
because animals too produce indivisible sounds, but none of
them are what I call a phoneme.

Phonemes are classified as vowels, fricatives, and mutes. 25
A vowel is an audible sound without contact between the
organs of speech; a fricative is an audible sound which does
involve such contact (for example, s and r); a mute involves such
contact but makes no audible sound unless it is combined
with a phoneme which does have audible sound (such as g, d). 30
Phonemes differ from each other in several ways: the shape of

the mouth; the point of contact of the organs; and the presence or absence of aspiration. They also differ by being long or short, and by having acute, grave, or intermediate pitch. Detailed discussion of these differences belongs to the theory of metre.

35 A syllable is a composite sound, made up of a mute and a sounding phoneme, that does not have a meaning in itself. *Gr* without an *a* is not a syllable* but becomes one with an *a*, namely *gra*. The various forms of syllable also belong to the theory of metre

A particle is a sound, without meaning in itself, that neither 1457a helps nor hinders the creation of a single semantic unit from two or more such units. It is meant to stand in the middle or at the end of a sentence, but may not stand at the beginning. Examples are *men*, *dh*, *toi*, and *de*.* Another kind of sound that 5 lacks meaning in itself is capable of forming a single semantic unit from several semantic units that share a single meaning. A conjunction is a sound lacking meaning itself that marks the beginning, the end, or the division of a sentence: for instance, *amphi*, *peri*, and so on.* Another such sound neither helps nor hinders the creation of a single semantic unit from two or more such units. It is meant to stand in the middle or at the end of a sentence, but may not stand at the beginning.

10 A noun* is a compound sound, lacking tense but bearing a meaning, no part of which is meaningful in its own right. (In composite nouns we do not treat any part as independently meaningful: 'dorus' in 'Theodorus' has no meaning.)

A verb is a compound sound bearing tense as well as mean-15 ing, no part of which is meaningful in its own right (just as with nouns). Words like 'man' or 'white' do not indicate time, but 'walks' and 'walked' indicate present and past tense respectively.

Verbs and nouns have inflections. With nouns, the inflections signify the case (the genitive 'of', the dative 'to', and so 20 on) or the number (singular 'man', plural 'men'). With verbs, the inflections signify things like the moods. The interrogative ('did he walk?') and imperative ('walk!') provide examples.*

A sentence is a compound significant sound which has a part or parts that have meaning in their own right. Not every sentence consists of a verb and a noun—a definition of 'man' 25 might not. There can be a sentence lacking any verb, but there must also be a part which has meaning on its own, for example, 'Cleon' in 'Cleon is walking'.

There are two ways in which sentences can be made into a unity: they may have just a single meaning, or they may simply be joined up together. The *Iliad* forms a unity in the latter sense, the definition of 'man' in the former. 30

The classification of nouns

21. Nouns come in two kinds, simple or double. Ones that have no parts that are meaningful—for example, 'earth'— I call 'simple'. Double nouns again come in two kinds: those that have two meaningful parts, and those that are composed of one meaningful and one non-meaningful part (though neither part has any meaning within the noun itself). There can also be triple, quadruple, and multiplex nouns, like many from Marseilles, such as 'Hermocaicoxanthus'.*

Every noun can also be classified in a different manner. 1457b There are ordinary words, foreign words, metaphorical terms, euphemisms, and coinages. Again, a noun may be lengthened, or shortened, or modified.

An ordinary word is one that is in general use in a community, a foreign word one that is in general use elsewhere. Obviously the same word may be both ordinary and foreign, but not in the same community: for instance, *sigunon* is the ordinary 5 word for spear in Cyprus, but is foreign to us; 'spear' is an ordinary word for us but foreign for them.

Metaphor is applying to something a noun that properly applies to something else. The transfer may be from genus to species, from species to genus, or from species to species; or it may be a case of analogy. *

If someone says 'My ship stopped here', I call that a transfer 10

from genus to species, because mooring is one kind of stopping.*
'Odysseus wrought in truth ten thousand noble needs' is transfer
from species to genus: 'ten thousand', a specific large number,
is used instead of the generic 'many'. Examples of transfer from
species to species are 'drawing off the life with bronze' and 'cutting off with sharp bronze': here 'drawing off' means 'cutting'
and 'cutting' means 'drawing off'—both activities are kinds of
removal.

By analogy I mean the case where B is related to A as D is
to C; one can then speak of D instead of B or B instead of D.
Sometimes people add the thing to which the replaced term is
related. I mean, for instance, a wine bowl is to Dionysus what
a shield is to Ares, so you may call a wine bowl 'the spear of
Dionysus' or a shield 'the wine cup of Ares'. Or again, old age
is to life as evening is to day, so you can speak of evening as the
day's old age, or, like Empedocles, call old age the evening or
the twilight of life. Sometimes there is no current word for one
term of the analogy, and yet the analogy can be used. A sower
scatters seed-corn, the sun scatters rays of fire: the first is called
'sowing', the second has no name. Yet because the relation of
the sun to its rays is the same as that of the sower to his seed-
corn, the poet can speak of the sun 'sowing his divine fire'. Yet
another way of using this kind of metaphor is to refer to something by the transferred term minus one of its properties, as
one might call a shield not just 'the wine bowl of Ares' but 'the
wineless wine bowl of Ares'.*

A coinage is a word not in use in a community which is made
up by the poet himself; there seem to be a few examples, such
as 'sproutage' for horns and 'prayerman' for priest.

Next, lengthening and shortening. A noun is lengthened if
it has a long vowel instead of a short one, or if an extra syllable
is inserted; it is shortened if something is removed. Examples
of lengthening are *poleeos* for *poleos* and *Peleiadeo* for *Peleidou*.
Examples of shortening are *kri* for the Greek word for barley,
and *do* for the Greek word for house. In a famous line, 'from a
pair of eyes a single vision comes', the abbreviation *ops* is used

44

for the Greek word for vision.* Finally, what is modification? That is when you take a word as it stands, and then add some- 5 thing on to it—for example, 'his rightward breast' instead of 'his right breast'.

Nouns themselves are either masculine, feminine, or neuter. Masculine nouns are those ending in *nu*, *rho*, *sigma*, or the two letters that contain *sigma*, namely *psi* and *xi*. Feminine are those 10 that end in vowels that are always long (e.g. *eta* and *omega*), or among the vowels of variable length, in *alpha*. (So it turns out that there are just as many kinds of masculine nouns as of feminine nouns, since *psi* and *xi* are compounds of *sigma*.) No noun ends in a mute or in a short vowel; only three end in *iota* (*meli*, 15 *kommi*, *peperi*), and five in *upsilon*.* Neuter nouns end in these letters and in *nu* and *sigma*.

Excellence in poetic style

22. The best style is one that is clear without being vulgar. The clearest style is one that uses only common words, but that is vulgar, as the poetry of Cleophon and Sthenelus dem- 20 onstrate. On the other hand, the use of exotic expressions— foreign words, metaphor, lengthening, and anything else out of the ordinary—makes a style solemn and elevated beyond the norm. But if you compose entirely in this style, the result will be either paradox or gibberish—paradox if made up entirely of 25 metaphor, gibberish if made up of foreign words. The essence of paradox is to report actual facts by an impossible combination of terms. This cannot be done with ordinary words, but it can with metaphorical expressions—for example, 'I saw a man use fire to fasten bronze upon his fellow'.* Passages composed 30 entirely of foreign words produce gibberish. So what is needed is a mixture of these kinds of expression: the use of common words will produce clarity, and the use of exotic expressions (foreign words, metaphor, ornament, and the other items listed) will elevate the style above the vulgar.

A great contribution to a style that is both clear and elevated 1458b

45

is made by lengthenings, shortenings, and modifications. By its unfamiliarity the variation from common usage will elevate the style, but the features shared with everyday speech will pre-
5 serve clarity. Some people find fault with this style and mock Homer for it, but they are wrong to do so. (An example is the elder Euclid, who said that it was easy to write poetry if you can lengthen words whenever you like—he offered parodies such
10 as 'I saw Epichares walking to Marathon' and 'not mixing his Hellebore'.)* An obtrusive use of this style certainly produces a comic effect; moderation is needed here, but equally in the employment of other elements of style. The use of metaphors, foreign words, and the other devices in an inappropriate and
15 deliberately comic way would produce the same effect. The difference they make to epic, when used appropriately, can be observed if one takes a verse and substitutes common words for them. The truth of what I am saying can be observed in the particular cases of foreign words, metaphors, and the other devices, by this method of substituting common words. For in-
20 stance, Aeschylus and Euripides each composed the same iam-bic line, but the change of a single word, the substitution of a foreign for a common noun, made one line seem splendid and the other banal. Aeschylus wrote in his *Philoctetes*, 'the cancer that eats the flesh of my foot', and Euripides changed 'eats' to
25 'banquets on'. Again, in 'a lowly, lank, and loathsome man' one might substitute the words 'small, weak, and ugly'. And com-pare 'offering a misshapen chair and lowly table' with 'offering a bad chair and a little table'. Or again, 'the resounding shore'
30 with 'the noisy shore'.*

Ariphades ridiculed the tragedians for introducing expres-sions that no one would ever use in conversation, such as 'the palace from' instead of 'from the palace', 'of thine' and 'Achil-
1459a les round about' for 'round Achilles'. Ariphrades failed to real-ize that it is precisely by being out of the ordinary that such expressions elevate the style.*

All the items I have mentioned must be used in an appropri-
5 ate manner. This goes for double nouns and foreign words, but

above all the poet must be skilled in the use of metaphor. This is the one thing that cannot be learnt from others, and it is a sign of genius, since it involves a keen eye for similarities. Double nouns are particularly suited for dithyramb, foreign words for heroic verse, and metaphor for iambics. All the devices I have mentioned are in place in heroic verse, but in iambic verse, which is particularly close to conversation, the most appropriate ones are those that could also appear in prose—including metaphor and ornament as well as common words. 10

So much, then, for tragedy and imitation on the stage. 15

IV. EPIC

The whole and its parts

23. What of representation in verse that takes the form of narrative? The story should, as in tragedy, be constructed dramatically, that is, based on a single action that is whole and entire and that has a beginning, a middle, and an end. Only thus can epic, like a living organism, produce its own proper pleasure. 20 The stories should not be organized like histories which call for an exposition not of a single action but of a single period of time, with all the things that happened to one or more people during it, each with only a chance relationship to the others. The sea-fight at Salamis and the battle against the Carthaginians in Sicily occurred simultaneously, without converging on a single goal; so in successive periods of time one thing may come after another without any single outcome.* Most poets, however, probably compose in this way. 25

Homer's superlative talent, as I have said before, shows itself here as elsewhere. He did not try to cover the Trojan war in its entirety, even though it did have a beginning and an end, for the story would have been too long and difficult to take in at one view—or if curtailed in length, too complex in its variety. 30

35 Instead, he singled out one segment, using others as episodes to add variety—episodes such as the catalogue of ships and the like. Other poets write about a single person or a single period,

1459b or a single action made up of many parts. Thus the author of the *Cypria* and of the *Little Iliad*. What is the result? From the *Iliad* and the *Odyssey* only one or at most two tragedies can be made; but from the *Cypria* you could make many and from the

5 *Little Iliad* no less than eight: for instance, *The Trial at Arms*, *Philoctetes*, *Neoptolemus*, *Eurypylus*, *Going Begging*, *Spartan Women*, *Sack of Troy*, *Making Sail*, as well as *Sinon* and *Women of Troy*.*

24. Epic, moreover, must needs come in the same kinds as tragedy: simple or complex, and based on character or suffer-

10 ing. The component parts, too, must be the same, with the exception of song and spectacle: we need reversals, discoveries, and sufferings, as well as intelligence and style. Homer was the first to employ all of these, and he did so most satisfactorily. His two poems exemplify different structures: the *Iliad* is simple

15 and full of suffering, and the *Odyssey* is complex (full of identifications) and is based on character. In addition, he excels everyone in ideas and style.

Epic and tragedy compared

The difference between epic and tragedy lies in the metre and in the length of the plot. An adequate limitation of length has already been suggested: it must be possible to take the begin-

20 ning and the end in a single view. This would be the case if the plots were shorter than the older epics, but as long as a series of tragedies presented at a single session. But epic offers particular scope for the extension of length. In tragedy it is not possible to represent several parts of the story occurring

25 simultaneously, but only the one part on stage performed by the actors. But in epic the narrative form makes it possible to include many simultaneous incidents that, if germane to the issue, add weight to the poem. This gives epic the advantage

in achieving grandeur, in offering variety to the hearer, and in
diversifying the episodes, while uniformity quickly palls and 30
may cause tragedies to flop.

As for the metre, experience has shown the suitability of
heroic verse. If one were to try narrative imitation in one or
more of the other metres the incongruity would be manifest.
Heroic verse is the most solemn and stately metre, while the
iambic trimeter and the trochaic tetrameter are metres for
movement—the latter for dancing, and the former for action.*
(Hence heroic verse welcomes foreign words and metaphors, 35
because narrative is an exceptional form of representation.)
It would be even odder to combine these metres together, as
Chairemon did. For this reason, no one has composed a long 1460a
structure in any metre other than the heroic; as we have said,
the very nature of the thing teaches people to choose what is
most appropriate.

The excellence of Homer

Among all his other admirable qualities, Homer deserves praise 5
because he is the only epic poet who knows what he should do
in his own person. The poet should say as little as possible in
his own voice; for that is not what makes him a mimic. Other
poets are always coming forward in person, and engage in representation only rarely and briefly; whereas Homer, after a brief
preamble, brings on stage a man or woman or other person- 10
age—every one a character and none of them mere dummies.

Astonishment is certainly something that tragedy must
evoke—but the chief cause of astonishment is improbability,
and this is more feasible in epic because we do not actually see
the agent. The pursuit of Hector would seem ridiculous on 15
stage, with the Greeks, because Achilles is shaking his head,
standing still instead of joining in the chase, but in epic it ex-
cites no remark. Astonishment gives pleasure: evidence of this
is the fact that we all exaggerate when recounting events, hoping to please our audience.

49

Homer, more than anyone else, taught poets the right way
to tell falsehoods. That is by the fallacy of affirming the con-
20 sequent. When the existence or occurrence of A follows from
the existence of occurrence of B, people think that if B is the
case, A too exists or occurs—but that is a fallacy. Suppose that
A is not the case, but if it were the case B would follow, the poet
should insert B, and because our mind knows that B is true it
will draw the false inference that A. An example of this is the
25 bath scene in the *Odyssey*.

Probable impossibilities are to be preferred to implausible
possibilities. Stories should not be made up from incredible
parts. Ideally there should be nothing incredible, or failing that,
it should lie outside the narrative (like Oedipus not knowing
30 how Laius died) rather than inside the drama (like the report
of the Pythian Games in *Electra* or the man in the *Mysians*
who comes from Tegea to Mysia without saying a word). It is a
ridiculous excuse to say that leaving these elements out would
ruin the story; plots like this should never be constructed in
35 the first place.* Even in the *Odyssey* the incredible details in
the setting ashore of Odysseus would be manifestly intolerable
1460b if treated by an inferior poet. As it is, Homer uses his other
talents to soften and conceal the incredibility.

Style needs particular attention in quiet passages where little
is happening and there is no expression of character or intelligence; a brilliant style, on the other hand, obscures character
5 and ideas.

How to respond to Homer's critics

25. Now for problems and solutions.* Consider the matter in
the following way and you will see how many there are and the
kinds in which they come.

The poet, like a painter or any other image-maker, is engaged
in representation, and there are three kinds of thing that he is
representing: things that are or were the case, things that are
10 said or thought to be the case, and things that ought to be the

case. These are expressed in a style that includes foreign words, metaphors, and the various modifications that poets are licensed to make. The criterion of correctness is not the same in poetry as in ethics, and not the same in poetry as in any other art. But within poetry itself two kinds of error are possible, one intrinsic 15 and the other incidental. If the poet meant to represent something and failed through incompetence, the fault is intrinsic.* But if he deliberately chooses to misrepresent—for example, to show a horse galloping with both right legs forward—the error is not a fault in the poetry, but a sin against some other art such as medicine. These, then, are the principles on which one 20 should confront and solve the objections posed by problems.

First, those relating to the art of poetry itself. If a poem contains impossibilities, that is a fault. However, the fault may be forgiven if they serve the purpose of the art, as specified earlier, that is to say, if they make this or some other part of the poem more impressive. A prime example is the pursuit of Hec- 25 tor. However, if the purpose could have been achieved better, or equally well, without violating the rules of the art, then the fault cannot be forgiven. If at all possible, no fault at all should be committed.

The question may be raised: if there is a fault, where is it located? Is it a violation of the poetic art, or is it something 30 incidental? It is less serious to be ignorant of the fact that a female deer has no horns than to paint a poor representation of one.

If the objection is that something is not true, then perhaps it is something that ought to be true. That was the answer that Sophocles gave when he said that while Euripides portrayed men as they actually are, he himself portrayed them as they 35 ought to be. That is the right response.

If neither response is possible, then the response must be that it accords with popular opinion.

The stories about the gods, for instance, may be, as Xeno- 1461a phanes says, neither true nor edifying; none the less they are current. In other cases it is not a matter of edification, but a

reflection of past practice: when we read 'the spears stood upright on their butt-end', that was the custom in those days, as it
still is among the Illyrians.

5   To determine whether something said or done was good or
bad you have to look not only at the actual deeds or words, but
also at the identity of the person saying or doing the thing, the
person to whom he said or did it, plus the occasion, the means,
and the motive (for example, whether it was to achieve a greater
good or avert a greater evil).

Other criticisms are to be met by considerations of style.
10 The foreign word *oureis* in the passage 'first against the *oureis*'
perhaps means not 'mules' but 'guards'. When we are told that
Dolon was ugly in appearance, perhaps this does not mean that
he was deformed, but simply plain-featured, since the Cretans
15 call facial beauty 'beauty of appearance'. The command 'mix it
stronger' need not mean 'serve the wine neat', as for drunkards,
but simply mix it faster. Other things are said metaphorically,
for instance, 'all gods and men slept through the night' when
at the same time he says 'when he looked over the Trojan plain
he marvelled at the sound of flutes and pipes'—here 'all' is
20 said metaphorically for 'many', since 'all' is a subset of 'many'.
Metaphorical too is 'alone without a share', a person who is
best known is unique. In some cases, as Hippias of Thasos
suggested, difficulties may be removed by a change of accen-
tuation, as 'We allow the granting of his prayer' and 'the part
the rain has rotted'. Sometimes punctuation does the trick, as
25 in Empedocles' 'On a sudden, things once immortal mortal
became, and things unmixed once mixed'. On other occasions,
it is ambiguity: in 'more of the night had passed', 'more' is
ambiguous.*

One can appeal to linguistic usage. People call diluted wine
'wine' and in the same way Homer speaks of 'a greave of
new-forged tin'. We call ironworkers 'bronze-smiths', and in
30 the same way Ganymede is said to pour wine for Zeus even
though the gods do not drink wine. (This last case could also
be metaphorical.)

Whenever a term seems to bear a sense that is contradictory, one should consider how many senses it might bear in the context. For instance, in 'By it was the bronze spear stopped', we should ask in how many different ways it might be stopped, and choose, among the alternatives, the one that gives the best sense. This is the exact opposite of the fault of which Glaucon complains, when people adopt unreasonable prejudices and deduce consequences, and if something in the text goes against their verdict they criticize the poet as if he had actually stated what they happen to believe. This is what happened in the case of Icarius. Some people think he was a Spartan. If so, they say, it is very odd that Telemachus did not meet him when he went to Sparta.* But the Cephallenians say that Odysseus' wife came from a Cephallenian family, and that her father's name was Icadius, not Icarius, and perhaps they are right. So probably the problem is created by a mistake of the critics.

In general, impossibilities should be justified by reference to the needs of poetry, the desire for edification, or the prevalence of an opinion. The needs of poetry make what is plausible though impossible preferable to what is possible but implausible. Perhaps it is not possible* for people to look the way Zeuxis painted them, but that is an idealization of the truth, and the artist should improve upon the model. Implausibilities should either be justified by their conformity to prevalent opinion, or made plausible by the defence that it is probable that some improbable things will occur.

Contradictory statements should be scrutinized in the same way as arguments rebutting a philosophical position. Is the same thing said, about the same thing, and in the same sense?

Is the poet contradicting something he has said himself, or something a reasonable person would assume?

It is, however, right to object to implausibility and immorality when they are unnecessary and serve no dramatic purpose. Aegeus in Euripides* provides an example of such implausibility, and Menelaus in *Orestes* provides an example of such immorality.

The objections of critics, then, come under five heads: impossibility, implausibility, immorality, self-contradiction, and violation of artistic standards. They are to be answered un-
25 der the heads I have set out, which add up to twelve.

The inferiority of epic to tragedy

The question may be asked whether epic or tragic representation is superior. If 'superior' means less vulgar, and an art is the less vulgar the more superior the public it addresses, it is utterly clear that an art which represents indiscriminately is vulgar. Actors believe that the audience is incapable of understanding anything unless they emphasize it, and so they go in for exag-
30 gerated motions—poor flute-players spin round if they have to show a discus being thrown, and they manhandle the conductor if the piece is about Scylla. Well, tragedy is like that—just as more recent actors were in the opinion of their predecessors. Mynniscus used to call Callippides an ape because of his over-
35 acting, and people took a similar view of Pindarus too.* The
1462a tragic art as a whole stands in the same relation to epic as the recent actors did to their predecessors. Critics say that epic addresses a decent public which does not need gestures, whereas tragedy addresses a public that is debased. If, then, tragedy is vulgar, it will manifestly be inferior.

First of all, this charge is laid not against the art of poetry,
5 but against the art of performance. In reciting epic poetry too it is possible to overdo gestures, like Sosistratus; so too in a song recital, as Mnasitheus of Opus used to do.

Next, not all movement is to be condemned, any more than all dancing, but only that of debased people, which was the
10 complaint against Callippides (and now against other actors too) for portraying women who were not respectable.

Again, tragedy, no less than epic, produces its effect even without movement; its quality is apparent from a mere reading. So if it is superior in other respects this charge need not damage it.

Further, there is nothing that epic has that tragedy does not also have—it can even use the same metre—but tragedy has a 15 substantial extra element in the form of music, which is a source of intense pleasure. It offers verisimilitude when read no less than when performed. Tragedy achieves the purpose of representation in a shorter space, and the pleasure is greater through being more concentrated rather than diluted over a long time. 1462b Suppose someone were to expand Sophocles'*Oedipus* into as many lines as the *Iliad*!

Again, epic poets offer a less unified representation. (Evidence of this is that one epic provides material for several 5 tragedies.) If they present a single story, it will seem either truncated if told briefly, or feeble if the telling is as long as is appropriate to epic metre. What I have in mind here is a plot containing many actions. The *Iliad* and the *Odyssey* have many such parts, each on a considerable scale; yet the poems are 10 structured as well as they possibly could, and are as close as possible to the representation of a single action.

Tragedy, then, excels in all these respects and also in artistic effect—remember that it is not just any pleasure, but a specific one, that these two genres should produce. So, since it achieves its purpose better, it is superior to epic. 15

So much, then, about tragedy and epic, their kinds and parts, and the differences between them; so much also for the causes of their success and failure, and how to answer the criticisms made of them.

SIR PHILIP SIDNEY

AN APOLOGY FOR POETRY

From *An Apology for Poetry*

Truly, to all them that, professing learning, inveigh against poetry, may justly be objected that they go very near to ungratefulness, to seek to deface that which, in the noblest nations and languages that are known, hath been the first light-giver to ignorance, and first nurse, whose milk by little and little enabled them to feed afterwards of tougher knowledges. And will they now play the hedgehog, that, being received into the den, drove out his host? Or rather the vipers, that with their birth kill their parents? Let learned Greece in any of her manifold sciences be able to show me one book before Musaeus,* Homer, and Hesiod, all three nothing else but poets. Nay, let any history be brought that can say any writers were there before them, if they were not men of the same skill, as Orpheus, Linus,* and some others are named, who having been the first of that country that made pens deliverers of their knowledge to their posterity, may justly challenge to be called their fathers in learning. For not only in time they had this priority (though in itself antiquity be venerable) but went before them as causes, to draw with their charming sweetness the wild untamed wits to an admiration of knowledge. So as Amphion was said to move stones with his poetry to build Thebes, and Orpheus to be listened to by beasts, indeed stony and beastly people. So among the Romans were Livius Andronicus* and Ennius; so in the Italian language the first that made it aspire to be a treasure house of science were the poets Dante, Boccaccio, and Petrarch; so in our English were Gower and Chaucer, after whom, encouraged and delighted with their excellent foregoing, others have followed to beautify our mother-tongue, as well in the same kind as in other arts.

This did so notably show itself, that the philosophers of Greece durst not a long time appear to the world but under the masks of poets. So Thales, Empedocles, and Parmenides sang

their natural philosophy in verses; so did Pythagoras and Pho-
cylides their moral counsels; so did Tyrtaeus in war matters, and
Solon in matters of policy; or rather they, being poets, did exercise their delightful vein in those points of highest knowledge
which before them lay did to the world. For that wise Solon was
directly a poet it is manifest, having written in verse the notable
fable of the Atlantic Island which was continued by Plato.* And
truly even Plato whosoever well considereth, shall find in the
body of his work, though the inside and strength were philosophy, the skin, as it were, and beauty depended most of poetry.
For all standeth upon dialogues; wherein he feigneth many
honest burgesses of Athens to speak of such matters that, if
they had been set on the rack, they would never have confessed
them; besides his poetical describing the circumstances of their
meetings, as the well-ordering of a banquet, the delicacy of a
walk, with interlacing mere tales, as Gyges' Ring* and others,
which who knoweth not to be flowers of poetry did never walk
into Apollo's garden.

And even historiographers (although their lips sound of
things done, and verity be written in their foreheads) have been
glad to borrow both fashion and perchance weight of poets. So
Herodotus entitled his history by the name of the nine Muses;
and both he and all the rest that followed him either stole or
usurped of poetry their passionate describing of passions, the
many particularities of battles which no man could affirm, or,
if that be denied me, long orations put in the mouths of great
kings and captains, which it is certain they never pronounced.

So that truly neither philosopher nor historiographer could,
at the first, have entered into the gates of popular judgements,
if they had not taken a great passport of poetry; which in all
nations at this day, where learning flourisheth not, is plain to be
seen, in all which they have some feeling of poetry. In Turkey,
besides their lawgiving diviners they have no other writers but
poets. In our neighbour-country Ireland, where truly learning
goeth very bare, yet are their poets held in a devout reverence.
Even among the most barbarous and simple Indians, where no

writing is, yet have they their poets, who make and sing songs (which they call *areytos*), both of their ancestors' deeds and praises of their gods. A sufficient probability that, if ever learning come among them, it must be by having their hard dull wits softened and sharpened with the sweet delights of poetry; for until they find a pleasure in the exercises of the mind, great promises of much knowledge will little persuade them that know not the fruits of knowledge. In Wales, the true remnant of the ancient Britons, as there are good authorities to show the long time they had poets, which they called bards, so through all the conquests of Romans, Saxons, Danes, and Normans, some of whom did seek to ruin all memory of learning from among them, yet do their poets unto this day last; so as it is not more notable in soon beginning, than in long continuing.

But since the authors of most of our sciences were the Romans, and before them the Greeks, let us a little stand upon their authorities, but even so far as to see what names they have given unto this now scorned skill. Among the Romans a poet was called *vates*, which is as much as a diviner, foreseer, or prophet, as by his conjoined words *vaticinium* and *vaticinari*, is manifest; so heavenly a title did that excellent people bestow upon this heart-ravishing knowledge. [...]

But now let us see how the Greeks named it and how they deemed of it. The Greeks called him a Poet, which name hath, as the most excellent, gone through other languages. It cometh of this word *poiein*, which is 'to make'; wherein I know not whether by luck or wisdom we Englishmen have met with the Greeks in calling him a maker. Which name, how high and incomparable a title it is, I had rather were known by marking the scope of other sciences than by my partial allegation.

There is no art delivered unto mankind that hath not the works of nature for his principal object, without which they could not consist, and on which they so depend as they become actors and players, as it were, of what nature will have set forth. So doth the astronomer look upon the stars, and, by that he seeth, set down what order nature hath taken therein. So do the geometrician and the arithmetician in their diverse sorts of quantities. So doth the musician in times tell you which by nature agree, which not. The natural philosopher thereon hath his name, and the moral philosopher standeth upon the natural virtues, vices, and passions of man; and 'follow nature', saith he, 'therein, and thou shalt not err'. The lawyer saith what men have determined; the historian what men have done. The grammarian speaketh only of the rules of speech, and the rhetorician and logician, considering what in nature will soonest prove and persuade, thereon give artificial rules, which still are composed within the circle of a question, according to the proposed matter. The physician weigheth the nature of man's body, and the nature of things helpful or hurtful unto it. And the metaphysic, though it be in the second and abstract notions, and therefore be counted supernatural, yet doth he, indeed, build upon the depth of nature.

Only the poet, disdaining to be tied to any such subjection, lifted up with the vigour of his own invention, doth grow, in effect, into another nature, in making things either better than nature bringeth forth, or, quite anew, forms such as never were in nature, as the heroes, demi-gods, cyclops, chimeras, furies, and such like; so as he goeth hand in hand with Nature, not enclosed within the narrow warrant of her gifts, but freely ranging only within the zodiac of his own wit. Nature never set forth the earth in so rich tapestry as diverse poets have done; neither with pleasant rivers, fruitful trees, sweet-smelling flowers, nor whatsoever else may make the too-much-loved earth more lovely; her world is brazen, the poets only deliver a golden. [...]

Neither let it be deemed too saucy a comparison to balance the highest point of man's wit with the efficacy of nature; but rather give right honour to the Heavenly Maker of that maker, who, having made man to his own likeness, set him beyond and over all the works of that second nature. Which in nothing he showeth so much as in poetry, when, with the force of a divine breath, he bringeth things forth far surpassing her doings, with no small argument to the incredulous of that first accursed fall of Adam,—since our erected wit maketh us know what perfection is, and yet our infected will keepeth us from reaching unto it. But these arguments will by few be understood, and by fewer granted; thus much I hope will be given me, that the Greeks, with some probability of reason, gave him the name above all names of learning.

Now let us go to a more ordinary opening of him, that the truth may be the more palpable; and so, I hope, though we get not so unmatched a praise as the etymology of his names will grant, yet his very description, which no man will deny, shall not justly be barred from a principal commendation.

Poesy, therefore, is an art of imitation, for so Aristotle termeth it in his word *mimēsis*, that is to say a representing, counterfeiting, or figuring forth; to speak metaphorically, a speaking picture, with this end, to teach and delight. [...]

. . . it is not rhyming and versing that maketh a poet (no more than a long gown maketh an advocate, who, though he pleaded in armour, should be an advocate and no soldier), but it is that feigning notable images of virtues, vices, or what else, with that delightful teaching, which must be the right describing note to know a poet by. Although indeed the Senate of Poets hath chosen verse as their fittest raiment, meaning, as in matter they passed all in all, so in manner to go beyond them; not speaking (table-talk fashion, or like men in a dream) words as they chanceably fall from the mouth, but peizing* each syllable of each word by just proportion, according to the dignity of the subject.

Now, therefore, it shall not be amiss, first to weigh this latter sort of poetry by his works, and then by his parts; and if in neither of these anatomies he be condemnable, I hope we shall obtain a more favourable sentence. This purifying of wit, this enriching of memory, enabling of judgement, and enlarging of conceit, which commonly we call learning, under what name soever it come forth or to what immediate end soever it be directed, the final end is to lead and draw us to as high a perfection as our degenerate souls, made worse by their clayey lodgings, can be capable of. This, according to the inclination of man, bred man-formed impressions. For some that thought this felicity principally to be gotten by knowledge, and no knowledge to be so high or heavenly as acquaintance with the stars, gave themselves to astronomy; others, persuading themselves to be demi-gods if they knew the causes of things, became natural and supernatural philosophers. Some an admirable delight drew to music, and some the certainty of demonstration to the mathematics; but all, one and other, having this scope: to know and by knowledge to lift up the mind from the dungeon of the body to the enjoying his own divine essence. But when by the balance of experience it was found that the astronomer, looking to the stars, might fall into a ditch, that the inquiring philosopher might be blind in himself, and the mathematician might draw forth a straight line with a crooked heart; then lo! did proof, the overruler of opinions, make manifest, that all these are but serving sciences, which, as they have each a private end in themselves, so yet are they all directed to the highest end of the mistress-knowledge, by the Greeks called *architektonikē*, which stands, as I think, in the knowledge of a man's self, in the ethic and politic consideration, with the end of well-doing, and not of well-knowing only; even as the saddler's next end is to make a good saddle, but his further end to serve a nobler faculty, which is horsemanship; so the horseman's to soldiery; and the soldier to have not only the skill, but to perform the practice of a soldier. So that the ending end of all earthly learning being virtuous action, those skills that most serve to bring forth that have a most just title to be princes over all the rest; wherein, if we can show, the poet is worthy to have it before any other competitors.

Among whom as principal challengers step forth the moral philosophers; whom, me thinketh, I see coming toward me with a sullen gravity, (as though they could not abide vice by day-light), rudely clothed, for to witness outwardly their contempt of outward things; with books in their hands against glory, whereto they set their names; sophistically speaking against subtlety; and angry with any man in whom they see the foul fault of anger. These men, casting largess as they go of Definitions, Divisions, and Distinctions, with a scornful interrogative do soberly ask whether it be possible to find any path so ready to lead a man to virtue, as that which teacheth what virtue is, and teacheth it not only by delivering forth his very being, his causes and effects, but also by making known his enemy, Vice, which must be destroyed, and his cumbersome servant Passion, which must be mastered, by showing the generalities that containeth it, and the specialities that are derived from it; lastly, by plain setting down how it extendeth itself out of the limits of a man's own little world, to the government of families, and maintaining of public societies.

The historian scarcely giveth leisure to the moralist to say so much, but that he, laden with old mouse-eaten records, authorizing himself for the most part upon other histories, whose greatest authorities are built upon the notable foundation of hearsay; having much ado to accord different writers, and to pick truth out of partiality; better acquainted with a thousand years ago than with the present age, and yet better knowing how this world goeth than how his own wit runneth; curious for antiquities and inquisitive of novelties, a wonder to young folks and a tyrant in table-talk; denieth, in a great chafe, that any man for teaching of virtue and virtuous action is comparable to him. [...] 'The philosopher', saith he, 'teacheth a disputative virtue, but I do an active. His virtue is excellent in the danger-less Academy of Plato, but mine showeth forth her honourable face in the battles of Marathon, Pharsalia, Poitiers and Agincourt. He teacheth virtue by certain abstract considerations, but I only bid you follow the footing of them who have gone before you. Old-aged experience goeth beyond the fine-witted philosopher; but I give the experience of many ages. Lastly, if he make the song book, I put the learner's hand to the lute; and if he be the guide, I am the light.' Then would he allege you innumerable examples, conferring story by story, how much the wisest senators and princes have been directed by the credit of history, as Brutus, Alphonsus of Aragon (and who not, if need be?). At length the long line of their disputations maketh a point in this, that the one giveth the precept, and the other the example.

Now whom shall we find, since the question standeth for the highest form in the school of learning, to be the moderator? Truly, as me seemeth, the poet; and if not a moderator, even the man that ought to carry the title from them both, and much more from all other serving sciences. Therefore compare we the poet with the historian and the moral philosopher; and if he go beyond them both, no other human skill can match him. For as for the divine, with all reverence it is ever to be excepted, not only for having his scope as far beyond any of these as eternity exceedeth a moment, but even for passing each of these in themselves. And for the lawyer, though Jus be the daughter of Justice, and Justice the chief of virtues, yet because he seeketh to make men good *formidine poenae* than *virtutis amore*;* or, to say righter, does not endeavour to make men good, but that their evil hurt not others; having no care, so he be a good citizen, how bad a man he be; therefore, as our wickedness maketh him necessary, and necessity maketh him honourable, so is he not in the deepest truth to stand in rank with those, who all endeavour to take naughtiness away, and plant goodness even in the secretest cabinet of our souls. And these four are all that any way deal in that consideration of men's manners, which being the supreme knowledge, they that best breed it deserve the best commendation.

The philosopher therefore and the historian are they which would win the goal, the one by precept, the other by example; but both, not having both, do both halt. For the philosopher, setting down with thorny argument the bare rule, is so hard of utterance and so misty to be conceived, that one that hath no other guide but him shall wade in him till he be old, before he shall find sufficient cause to be honest. For his knowledge standeth so upon the abstract and the general, that happy is that man who may understand him, and more happy that can apply what he doth understand. On the other side, the historian, wanting the precept, is so tied, not to what should be but to what is, to the particular truth of things and not to the general reason of things, that his example draweth no necessary consequence, and therefore a less fruitful doctrine.

Now doth the peerless poet perform both; for whatsoever the philosopher saith should be done, he giveth a perfect picture of it in some one by whom he presupposeth it was done, so as he coupleth the general notion with the particular example. A perfect picture, I say, for he yieldeth to the powers of the mind an image of that wherof the philosopher bestoweth but the wordish description, which doth neither strike, pierce, nor possess the sight of the soul so much as that other doth. For as, in outward things, to a man that had never seen an elephant or a rhinoceros, who should tell him most exquisitely all their shapes, colour, bigness, and particular mark; or of a gorgeous palace, the architecture, with declaring the full beauties, might well make the hearer able to repeat, as it were by rote, all he had heard, yet should never satisfy his inward conceit with being witness to itself of a true lively knowledge; but the same man, as soon as he might see those beasts well painted, or that house well in model, should straightways grow, without need of any description, to a judicial comprehending of them: so no doubt the philosopher, with his learned definitions, be it of virtues or vices, matters of public policy or private government, replenisheth the memory with many infallible grounds of wisdom, which notwithstanding lie dark before the imaginative and judging power, if they be not illuminated or figured forth by the speaking picture of poesy. [...]

For conclusion, I say the philosopher teacheth, but he teacheth obscurely, so as the learned only can understand him; that is to say, he teacheth them that are already taught. But the poet is the food for the tenderest stomachs; the poet is indeed the right popular philosopher. Wherof Aesop's tales give good proof; whose petty allegories, stealing under the formal tales of beasts, make many, more beastly than beasts, begin to hear the sound of virtue from those dumb speakers.

But now may be it alleged that if this imagining of matters be so fit for the imagination then must the historian needs surpass, who bringeth you images of true matters, such as indeed were done, and not such as fantastically or falsely may be suggested to have been done. Truly, Aristotle himself, in his Discourse of poesy, plainly determineth this question, saying that poetry is *philosophōteron* and *spoudaioteron*, that is to say, it is more philosophical and more studiously serious than history. His reason is, because poesy dealeth with *katholou,* that is to say with the universal consideration, and the history with *kat' hekaston*, the particular. 'Now', saith he, 'the universal weighs what is fit to be said or done, either in likelihood or necessity, which the poesy considereth in his imposed names; and the particular only marketh whether Alcibiades did, or suffered, this or that': thus far Aristotle. Which reason of his, as all his, is most full of reason. [...]

So, then, the best of the historian is subject to the poet; for whatsoever action or faction, whatsoever counsel, policy, or war-stratagem the historian is bound to recite, that may the poet, if he list, with his imitation make his own, beautifying it both for further teaching and more delighting, as it pleaseth him; having all, from Dante's heaven to his hell, under the authority of his pen. Which if I be asked what poets have done so? as I might well name some, yet say I, and say again, I speak of the art, and not of the artificer. [...]

I conclude, therefore, that he excelleth history, not only in furnishing the mind with knowledge, but in setting it forward to that which deserveth to be called and accounted good; which setting forward, and moving to well-doing, indeed setteth the laurel crown upon the poet as victorious, not only of the historian, but over the philosopher, howsoever in teaching it may be questionable. For suppose it be granted (that which I suppose with great reason may be denied) that the philosopher, in respect of his methodical proceeding, doth teach more perfectly than the poet, yet do I think that no man is so *philophilosophos* as to compare the philosopher in moving with the poet. And that moving is of a higher degree than teaching, it may by this appear, that it is well nigh both the cause and the effect of teaching; for who will be taught, if he be not moved with desire to be taught? And what so much good doth this teaching bring forth (I speak still of moral doctrine) as that it moveth one to do that which it doth teach? For, as Aristotle saith, it is not *gnōsis* but *praxis* must be the fruit; and how *praxis* can be, without being moved to practise, it is no hard matter to consider. The philosopher showeth you the way, he informeth you of the particularities, as well as the tediousness of the way, as of the pleasant lodging you shall have when your journey is ended, as of the many by-turnings that may divert you from your way; but this is to no man but to him that will read him, and read him with attentive, studious painfulness; which constant desire whoever hath in him, hath already passed half the hardness of the way, and therefore is beholding to the philosopher but for the other half. Nay, truly, learned men have learnedly thought, that when once reason hath so much overmastered passion as that the mind hath a free desire to do well, the inward light each mind hath in itself is as good as a philosopher's book; since in nature we know it is well to do well, and what is well and what is evil, although not in the words of art which philosophers bestow upon us; for out of natural conceit the philosophers drew it. But to be moved to do that which we know, or to be moved with desire to know, *hoc opus, hic labor est.**

Now therefore of all sciences, (I speak still of human, and according to the human conceit) is our poet the monarch. For he doth not only show the way, but giveth so sweet a prospect into the way as will entice any man to enter into it. Nay, he doth, as if your journey should lie through a fair vineyard, at the very first give you a cluster of grapes, that full of that taste you may long to pass further. He beginneth not with obscure defin-itions, which must blur the margin with interpretations, and load the memory with doubtfulness. But he cometh to you with words set in delightful proportion, either accompanied with, or prepared for, the well-enchanting skill of music; and with a tale, forsooth, he cometh unto you, with a tale which holdeth children from play, and old men from the chimney-corner; and pretending no more, doth intend the winning of the mind from wickedness to virtue; even as the child is often brought to take most wholesome things, by hiding them in such other as have a pleasant taste, which if one should begin to tell them the nature of the aloes or rhubarb they should receive, would sooner take their physic at their ears than at their mouth. [...]

Where the philosophers, as they scorn to delight, so must they be content little to move, saving wrangling whether virtue be the chief or only good, whether the contemplative or the active life do excel, which Plato and Boethius well knew, and there-fore made Mistress Philosophy very often borrow the mask-ing raiment of Poesy. For even those hard-hearted evil men who think virtue a school-name, and know no other good but *indulgere genio*,* and therefore despise the austere admonitions of the philosopher, and feel not the inward reason they stand upon, yet will be content to be delighted, which is all the good-fellow poet seemeth to promise; and so steal to see the form of goodness (which seen, they cannot but love) ere themselves be aware, as if they took a medicine of cherries.

Infinite proofs of the strange effects of this poetical inven-tion might be alleged; only two shall serve, which are so often remembered as I think all men know them. The one of Mene-nius Agrippa,* who, when the whole people of Rome had reso-lutely divided themselves from the senate, with apparent show of utter ruin, though he were, for that time, an excellent orator, came not among them upon trust either of figurative speeches or cunning insinuations, and much less with far-fetched maxims of philosophy, which (especially if they were Platonic) they must have learned geometry before they could well have conceived; but, forsooth, he behave himself like a homely and familiar poet. He telleth them a tale, that there was a time when all the parts of the body made a mutinous conspiracy against the belly, which they thought devoured the fruits of each other's labour; they concluded they would let so unprofitable a spender starve. In the end, to be short—for the tale is notorious, and as notorious that it was a tale—with punishing the belly they plagued themselves. This, applied by him, wrought such effect in the people, as I never read that ever words brought forth but then so sudden and so good an alteration; for upon reasonable conditions a perfect reconciliation ensued.

The other is of Nathan the prophet,* who, when the holy David had so far forsaken God as to confirm adultery with murder, when he was to do the tenderest office of a friend, in laying his own shame before his eyes, (sent by God to call again so chosen a servant) how doth he it but by telling of a man whose beloved lamb was ungratefully taken from his bosom? The application most divinely true, but the discourse itself feigned; which made David (I speak of the second and instrumental cause) as in a glass to see his own filthiness, as that heavenly Psalm of Mercy* well testifieth.

By these, therefore, examples and reasons, I think it may be manifest that the poet, with that same hand of delight, doth draw the mind more effectually than any other art doth. And so a conclusion not unfitly ensueth: that as virtue is the most excellent resting-place for all worldly learning to make his end of, so poetry, being the most familiar to teach it, and most princely to move towards it, in the most excellent work is the most excellent workman.

PERCY BYSSHE SHELLEY

A DEFENCE OF POETRY

From *A Defence of Poetry*

The connection of scenic exhibitions with the improvement or corruption of the manners of men has been universally recognized: in other words the presence or absence of poetry in its most perfect and universal form, has been found to be connected with good and evil in conduct or habit. The corruption which has been imputed to the drama as an effect begins when the poetry employed in its constitution ends: I appeal to the history of manners whether the periods of the growth of one and the decline of the other have not corresponded with an exactness equal to any example of moral cause and effect.

The drama at Athens, or wheresoever else it may have approached to its perfection, ever co-existed with the moral and intellectual greatness of the age. The tragedies of the Athenian poets are as mirrors in which the spectator beholds himself, under a thin disguise of circumstance, stripped of all but that ideal perfection and energy which every one feels to be the internal type of all that he loves, admires, and would become. The imagination is enlarged by a sympathy with pains and passions so mighty, that they distend in their conception the capacity of that by which they are conceived; the good affections are strengthened by pity, indignation, terror and sorrow; and an exalted calm is prolonged from the satiety of this high exercise of them into the tumult of familiar life: even crime is disarmed of half its horror and all its contagion by being represented as the fatal consequence of the unfathomable agencies of nature; error is thus divested of its wilfulness; men can no longer cherish it as the creation of their choice. In the drama of the highest order here is little food for censure or hatred; it teaches rather self-knowledge and self-respect. Neither the eye nor the mind can see itself, unless reflected upon that which it resembles. The drama, so long as it continues to express poetry, is a prismatic and many-sided mirror, which collects the brightest rays of human nature and divides and reproduces them from the simplicity of their elementary forms, and touches them with majesty and beauty, and multiplies all that it reflects, and endows it with the power of propagating its like wherever it may fall.

But in periods of the decay of social life, the drama sympathizes with that decay. Tragedy becomes a cold imitation of the form of the great masterpieces of antiquity, divested of all harmonious accompaniment of the kindred arts; and often the very form misunderstood, or a weak attempt to teach certain doctrines which the writer considers as moral truths; and which are usually no more than specious flatteries of some gross vice or weakness with which the author, in common with his auditors, are infected. Hence what has been called the classical and domestic drama. Addison's *Cato** is a specimen of the one; and would it were not superfluous to cite examples of the other! To such purposes poetry cannot be made subservient. Poetry is a sword of lightning, ever unsheathed, which consumes the scabbard that would contain it. And thus we observe that all dramatic writings of this nature are unimaginative in a singular degree; they affect sentiment and passion, which, divested of imagination, are other names for caprice and appetite. The period in our own history of the grossest degradation of the drama is the reign of Charles II, when all forms in which poetry had been accustomed to be expressed became hymns to the triumph of kingly power over liberty and virtue. Milton stood alone illuminating an age unworthy of him. At such periods the calculating principle pervades all the forms of dramatic exhibition, and poetry ceases to be expressed upon them. Comedy loses its ideal universality: wit succeeds to humour; we laugh from self-complacency and triumph, instead of pleasure; malignity, sarcasm and contempt succeed to sympathetic merriment; we hardly laugh, but we smile. Obscenity, which is ever blasphemy against the divine beauty in life, becomes, from the very veil which it assumes, more active if less disgusting: it is a monster for which the corruption of society for ever brings forth new food, which it devours in secret.

The drama being that form under which a greater number of modes of expression of poetry are susceptible of being combined than any other, the connection of poetry and social good is more observable in the drama than in whatever other form. And it is indisputable that the highest perfection of human society has ever corresponded with the highest dramatic excellence; and that the corruption or the extinction of the drama in a nation where it has once flourished, is a mark of corruption of manners, and an extinction of the energies which sustain the soul of social life. But, as Machiavelli says of political institutions, that life may be preserved and renewed, if men should arise capable of bringing back the drama to its principles. And this is true with respect to poetry in its most extended sense: all language, institution and form, require not only to be produced but to be sustained: the office and character of a poet participates in the divine nature as regards providence, no less than as regards creation.

DOROTHY L. SAYERS

ARISTOTLE ON
DETECTIVE FICTION

From 'Aristotle on Detective Fiction'

LECTURE DELIVERED AT OXFORD, 5 MARCH 1935

Some twenty-five years ago it was rather the fashion among commentators to deplore that Aristotle should have so much inclined to admire a kind of tragedy that was not, in their opinion, 'the best'. All this stress laid on the plot, all this hankering after melodrama and surprise—was it not rather unbecoming—rather inartistic? Psychology for its own sake was just then coming to the fore, and it seemed almost blasphemous to assert that 'they do not act in order to portray the characters; they include the characters for the sake of the action'. Indeed we are not yet free from the influence of that school of thought for which the best kind of play or story is that in which nothing particular happens from beginning to end.

Now, to anyone who reads the *Poetics* with an unbiased mind, it is evident that Aristotle was not so much a student of his own literature as a prophet of the future. He criticised the contemporary Greek theatre because it was, at that time, the most readily available, widespread and democratic form of popular entertainment presented for his attention. But what, in his heart of hearts, he desired was a good detective story; and it was not his fault, poor man, that he lived some twenty centuries too early to revel in the Peripeties of *Trent's Last Case* or the Discoveries of *The Hound of the Baskervilles*.* He had a stout appetite for the gruesome. 'Though the objects themselves may be painful', says he, 'we delight to view the most realistic representations of them in art, the forms, for example, of the lowest animals and of dead bodies.' The crawling horror of *The Speckled Band* would, we infer, have pleased him no less than *The Corpse in the Car*, *The Corpse in Cold Storage* or *The Body in the Silo*. Yet he was no thriller fan. 'Of simple plots and actions', he rightly observes, 'the episodic are the worst. I call a plot episodic when there is neither probability nor necessity in the sequence of the episodes.' […] He maintained that dreadful and alarming events produced their best effect when they occurred, 'unexpectedly', indeed, but also 'in consequence of one another.' In one phrase he sums up the whole essence of the detective story proper. Speaking of the denouement of the work, he says: 'It is also possible to discover whether some one has done or not done something.' Yes, indeed.

Now it is well known that a man of transcendent genius, though working under difficulties and with inadequate tools, will do more useful and inspiring work than a man of mediocre intellect with all the resources of the laboratory at his disposal. Thus Aristotle, with no better mysteries for his study than the sordid complications of the Agamemnon family, no more scientific murder-methods than the poisoned arrow of Philoctetes or the somewhat improbable medical properties of Medea's cauldron; with detective heroes so painfully stereotyped and unsympathetic as the inhuman array of gods from the machine, yet contrived to hammer out from these unpromising elements a theory of detective fiction so shrewd, all-embracing and practical that the *Poetics* remains the finest guide to the writing of such fiction that could be put, at this day, into the hands of an aspiring author.

In what, then, does this guidance consist? From the start Aristotle accepts the Detective Story as a worthy subject for serious treatment. 'Tragedy' he observes (tragedy being the literary form which the detective story took in his day) 'also acquired magnitude—that is, it became important both in form and substance. 'Discarding short stories and a ludicrous diction, it assumed, though only at a late point in its progress, a tone of dignity.' I am afraid that 'short stories and a ludicrous diction' have characterised some varieties of the genre up to a very late point indeed; it is true, however, that there have recently been great efforts at reform. Aristotle then goes on to define tragedy in terms excellently applicable to our subject; 'The imitation' (or presentment, or representation—we will not quarrel over the word) 'of an action that is serious'—it will be admitted that murder is an action of a tolerably serious nature—'and also complete in itself'—that is highly important, since a detective story that leaves any loose ends is no proper detective story at all—'with incidents arousing pity and fear, wherewith to accomplish its catharsis of such emotions.'

Too much has already been said and written on the vexed subject of the catharsis. Is it true, as magistrates sometimes assert, that little boys go to the bad through reading detective stories? Or is it, as detective writers prefer to think with Aristotle, that in a nerve ridden age the study of crime stories provides a safety valve for the bloodthirsty passions that might otherwise lead us to murder our spouses? Of all forms of modern fiction, the detective story alone makes virtue *ex hypothesi* more interesting than vice, the detective more beloved than the criminal. But there is a dangerous error going about—namely that 'if... detective fiction leads to an increase in crime, then the greater the literary merit, the greater will be the corresponding increase in crime'. Now this is simply not true: few people can have been inspired to murder their uncles by the literary merits of *Hamlet*. On the contrary, where there is no beauty there can be no catharsis; an ill-written book, like an ill-compounded drug, only irritates the system without purging. Let us then see to it that, if we excite evil passions, it is so done as to sublimate them at the same time by the contemplation of emotional or intellectual beauty. Thus far, then, concerning the catharsis.

Aristotle next discusses Plot and Character. 'A detective story', we gather, 'is impossible without action, but there may be one without character.' A few years ago, the tendency was for all detective stories to be of the characterless or 'draughtboard' variety; to-day, we get many examples exhibiting a rather slender plot and a good deal of morbid psychology. Aristotle's warning, however, still holds good.

One may string together a series of characteristic speeches of the utmost finish as regards diction and thought, and yet fail to produce the true dramatic effect; but one will have much better success with a story which, however inferior in these respects, has a plot.

And again:

The first essential, the life and soul, so to speak, of the detective story is the plot and the characters come second.

As regards the make-up of the plot, Aristotle is again very helpful. He says firmly that it should have a beginning, a middle and an end. Herein the detective story is sharply distinguished from the kind of modern novel which, beginning at the end, rambles backwards and forwards without particular direction and ends on an indeterminate note, and for no ascertainable reason except the publisher's refusal to provide more printing and paper for seven-and-sixpence. The detective story commonly begins with the murder; the middle is occupied with the detection of the crime and the various peripeties or reversals of fortune arising out of this; the end is the discovery and execution of the murderer—than which nothing can very well be more final. Our critic adds that the work should be of a convenient length. If it is too short, he says, our perception of it becomes indistinct. [...] He objects, still more strongly to the work that is of vast size, or 'one thousand miles long'. 'A story or plot', he reminds us, 'must be of some length, but of a length to be taken in by the memory.' A man *might* write a detective story of the length of *Ulysses*,* but, if he did, the reader would not be able to bear all the scattered clues in mind from the first chapter to the last, and the effect of the final discovery would be lost. In practice, a length from 80,000 to 120,000 words is desirable, if the book is to sell; and this is enough to allow, in Aristotle's general formula, of 'the hero's passing by a series of probable or necessary stages from misfortune to happiness or from happiness to misfortune'. Later, however, he conveys a very necessary warning: 'A writer often stretches out a plot beyond its capabilities, and is thus obliged to twist the sequence of incident.' It is unwise to 'write-up' a short-story type of plot to novel length, even to fulfil a publisher's contract.

The next section of the *Poetics* gives advice about the unity of the plot. It is not necessary to tell us everything that ever befell the hero. For example, says Aristotle, 'in writing about Sherlock Holmes' (I have slightly adapted the instance he gives)

the author does not trouble to say where the hero was born, or whether he was educated at Oxford or Cambridge, nor does he enter into details about incidents which—though we know they occurred—are not relevant to the matter in hand, such as the cases of Vamberry the Wine Merchant, the Aluminium Crutch, Wilson the Notorious Canary-Trainer or Isadora Persano and the Remarkable Worm.

The story, he says

must represent one action, a complete whole, with its several incidents so closely connected that the transposal or withdrawal of any one of them will disjoin and dislocate the whole.

In other words, 'murder your darlings'—or, if you must write a purple passage, take care to include in it some vital clue to the solution which cannot be omitted or transposed to any other part of the story. [...]

Concerning the three necessary parts of a detective story—peripety, or reversal of fortune, discovery and suffering—Aristotle has many very just observations. On suffering, we need not dwell long. Aristotle defines it as 'action of a destructive or painful nature, such as murders, tortures, woundings and the like'. These are common enough in the detective story and the only remark to be made is that they ought always to help on the action in some way and not be put in merely to harrow the feelings, still less to distract attention from a weakness in the plot.

A reversal of fortune may happen to all or any of the characters: the victim—who is frequently a man of vast wealth—may be reduced to the status of a mere dead body, or may, again, turn out not to be dead after all, as we had supposed. The wrongly suspected person, after undergoing great misfortunes, may be saved from the condemned cell and restored to the arms of his betrothed. The detective, after several errors of reasoning, may hit upon the right solution. Such peripeties keep the story moving and arouse alternating emotions of terror, compassion and so forth in the reader. These events are best brought about, not fortuitously, but by some *hamartia* or defect in the sufferer. The defect may be of various kinds. The victim may suffer on account of his unamiable character, or through the error of marrying a wicked person, or through foolishly engaging in dubious finance, or through the mistake of possessing too much money. The innocent suspect may have been fool enough to quarrel with the victim or to bring suspicion on himself by suppressing evidence with intent to shield somebody. The detective suffers his worries and difficulties through some failure of observation or logic. All these kinds of defect are fruitful in the production of Peripety. [...]

This brings us to the very remarkable passage in which Aristotle, by one of those blinding flashes of light which display to the critic of genius the very core and centre of the writer's problem, puts the whole craft of the detective writer into one master-word: *Paralogismos*. That word should be written up in letters of gold on the walls of every mystery-monger's study—at once the guiding star by which he sets his compass and the jack-o'lantern by which he leads his readers into the bog; paralogism,—the art of the false syllogism—for which Aristotle himself has a blunter and more candid phrase. Let us examine the whole paragraph, for it is of the utmost importance.

'Homer', says he—if he had lived in our own day he might have chosen some more apposite example, such as Father Knox* or Mrs Agatha Christie, but thinking no doubt of *Odysseus*, he says of Homer—'Homer more than any other has taught the rest of us the art of *framing lies in the right way*. I mean the use of paralogism. Whenever, if A is or happens a consequent B is or happens, men's notion is that if the B is the A also is—but that is a false conclusion. Accordingly if A is untrue, but there is something else, B, that on the assumption of its truth follows as its consequent, then the right thing is to present us with the B. Just because we know the truth of the consequent, we are in our own minds led on to the erroneous inference of the truth of the antecedent.'

There you are, then; there is your recipe for detective fiction: the art of framing lies. From beginning to end of your book, it is your whole aim and object to lead the reader up the garden; to induce him to believe a lie. To believe the real murderer to be innocent, to believe some harmless person to be guilty; to believe the detective to be right where he is wrong and mistaken when he is right; to believe the false alibi to be sound, the present absent, the dead alive and the living dead; to believe, in short, anything and everything but the truth. [...]

This brings us to the consideration of the characters, concerning which Aristotle takes a very twentieth-century point of view. He says that they must be *good*. This, I suppose, must be taken relatively, to mean that they should, even the meanest and wickedest of them, be not merely monsters and caricatures like the personages in a low farce, but endued with some sort of human dignity, so that we are enabled to take them seriously. They must also be *appropriate*: a female, he says, must not be represented as clever. [...] Thirdly, the characters must be *like the reality* (*to homoion*). Scholars differ about what Aristotle means by this word. Some think it means 'conformable to tradition'; that the villain should be easily recognizable as villainous by his green eyes, his moustache, and his manner of ejaculating 'Ha!' and the detective by his eccentricities, his pipe and his dressing-gown, after the more ancient models. But I do not agree with them, and believe that the word means, as we say to-day, 'realistic', i.e. with some moderate approximation in speech and behaviour to such men and women as we see about us. For elsewhere Aristotle takes the modern, realistic view, as when he says, for instance, that the plot ought not to turn on the detection and punishment of a hopelessly bad man who is villainous in all directions at once—forger, murderer, adulterer, thief,—like the bad baron in an Adelphi melodrama; but rather on that of an intermediate kind of person—a decent man with a bad kink in him—which is the kind of villain most approved by the best modern writers in this kind. For the more the villain resembles an ordinary man, the more shall we feel pity and horror at his crime and the greater will be our surprise at his detection. So, too, as regards the innocent suspects and the police; in treating all such characters a certain resemblance to real life is on the whole to be desired. Lastly, and most important and difficult of all, the characters must be *consistent* from first to last. Even though at the end we are to feel surprise on discovering the identity of the criminal, we ought not to feel incredulity; we should rather be able to say to ourselves: 'Yes, I can see *now* that from the beginning this man had it in him to commit murder, had I only had the wits to interpret the indications furnished by the author.'

A NOTE ON METRE

In several places Aristotle refers to particular verse metres. The metre of Greek poetry works on a different principle from that of English verse: whereas in English it is the stress that determines the metre, in Greek the metre depends on the length of the syllables. In spite of this, the differences between different metrical patterns exhibit a considerable resemblance in the two languages, so that it is not inappropriate to illustrate the metres for English readers with examples drawn from English poets and translators.

Hexameter is the metre of the Homeric epics. Each line has six units, or feet, which in most cases can be either dactyls (- ˘ ˘, i.e. long/short/short) or spondees (- -, i.e. long long). A typical line would be - - | - ˘ ˘ | - ˘ ˘ | - - | - ˘ ˘ | - -. Here is an English version of some lines of the Iliad, by A. H. Clough:

> So beseeching he said, and was heard of Phoebus Apollo
> Who from Olympus' heights' descending came full of anger.

Elegiac couplet consists of a hexameter followed by a pentameter, that is to say a five-foot line consisting of two parts, the first consisting of two feet, which may be dactyls or spondees, followed by one syllable and a pause, and the second consisting of two dactyls followed by a single syllable. Again A. H. Clough provides a good example in English at the beginning of his *Amours de Voyage*:

> Over the great windy waters, and over the clear crested summits
> Unto the sun and the sky, and unto the perfecter earth.

Iambic trimeter is the standard metre for speeches in tragedy. The basic foot is the iamb (˘ -), a short followed by a long. A line in tragic dialogue will consist of six iambs, with other feet allowed as substitutes in certain places. The Greek verse corresponds to the modern Alexandrine. Here is a translation of an exchange between Orestes and his sister in the recognition scene of Euripides' *Iphigeneia in Tauris*:

> IPH: What name was given you by the man who you begat?
> OR: If truth were told, none but Unhappy is my name.

Trochaic tetrameter is a four-foot line based on the trochee (- ˘), a long followed by a short., as in the mnemonic 'poky trochee makes me jokey'. The standard foot is a pair of trochees (with substitution allowed); the final foot is usually short of a syllable. The metre was popular in scurrilous verses and in comedy.

EXPLANATORY NOTES

PLATO, *REPUBLIC*

3 *Ouranos...upon him*: according to the primitive myth (Hesiod, *Theogony* 137 ff., 453 ff.) Kronos castrated his father Ouranos and swallowed his children.

4 *a pig*: the victim which had to be offered by everyone seeking to be initiated in the Eleusinian Mysteries.

7 *and he begged all the Acheans . . . generals of the host*: Iliad 1.15–16.

ARISTOTLE, *POETICS*

17 *dithyramb*: a choral lyric in honour of the god Dionysus.

18 *Sophron and Xenarchus*: father and son, Sicilian writers of prose comic skits in the latter half of the fifth century BC.

Socratic dialogues: elsewhere Aristotle often quotes Socratic utterances in Plato's dialogues as if they were Socrates' own words: here he shows an awareness that the dialogues involve creative writing. The point he is making is that there is no Greek word corresponding to our word 'prose' for a genre that includes both skits and dialogues.

or any other metre: similarly, there is no Greek word corresponding to our word 'verse' to cover all poems irrespective of their particular metre. Aristotle's overall conclusion is that it is content, not form, that settles whether something is poetry.

Empedocles: fifth-century Sicilian thinker who composed two volumes of natural philosophy in hexameter verse.

nomes: instrumental melodies to which texts could be improvised.

Polygnotus: was the most famous wall-painter of fifth-century Greece. Nothing is known for certain about the other two artists. Henceforth, no comment will be attached to names of persons known only from Aristotle's references.

19 *Deiliad*: the *Iliad* is an epic about Ilium (Troy); the *Deiliad*, therefore, will be an epic about Deilos ('The Coward').

Timotheus and Philoxenus: Timotheus of Miletus (*c*.450–*c*.360) wrote an account of the battle of Salamis in irregular verse; his contemporary Philoxenus wrote a dithyramb in which the Cyclops sang a solo to the lyre.

the Dorians: one of the three main branches of the Greek race, who occupied the Peloponnese and counted among their cities Megara (on the Gulf of Corinth) and several Sicilian colonies. Their dialect, Doric, differed from the Attic dialect spoken in Athens.

19 *Chionides and Magnes*: the earliest Attic comic poets, active about 475 BC.

20 *from childhood*: it is no accident that the word 'play' designates both childish pretending and dramatic performance.

'this is so-and-so': perhaps Aristotle has in mind not simply the recognition of the sitter of a portrait, but also the identification of a divine or mythical subject of a statue.

21 *Margites and similar poems*: modern scholars contest the accuracy of Aristotle's chonrological sketch. The *Margites* is a lost burlesque dubiously attributed to Homer.

phallic singing: in many Greek religious fertility festivals an icon of the male organ of generation was carried in procession.

22 *magistrate*: at Athens a city official, the archon, chose and funded plays for performance at the annual festival of Dionysus.

Crates: a fifth-century poet who wrote six plays, now lost. He won prizes in the Dionysia in 450 and later years.

23 *purification*: the Greek word *katharsis*, which occurs only here in the *Poetics*, is not defined by Aristotle and its meaning is much controverted. See Introduction, p. xxv.

obvious to everyone: in fact the Greek word corresponding to 'music-making' is ambiguous: it may mean either the composition or the performance of music.

25 *totally lacking in it*: the speciality of Zeuxis (late fifth century) was the representation of female beauty.

27 *taken place*: the Greek text is here uncertain.

28 *proper names*: a proper name stands for a particular individual, and both 'Alcibiades' and 'Oedipus' are, for Aristotle, proper names of actual people. Despite this, he tells us, the dramatist, unlike the historian, does not wish to give us information about a historic individual, but to convey general truths about human nature.

Alcibiades: a fifth-century Athenian politician whose erratic career is recorded in Thucydides' history of the Peloponnesian War.

Agathon's Antheus: Agathon was a distinguished dramatic poet who won his first victory in a dramatic competition in 416 BC; the banquet he gave in celebration provides the setting for Plato's *Symposium*. His plays, all now lost, are often quoted by Aristotle.

29 *defective stories*: the OCT text has 'simple stories', but emendation seems necessary.

pity and fear: Aristotle's reasons for singling out these emotions are discussed in the Introduction, p. xxvi.

reversal or a discovery or both: the Greek words *peripeteia* and *anagnorisis* are here given a technical meaning which Aristotle goes on to explain in later paragraphs.

30 *opposite effect*: in Sophocles' tragedy *King Oedipus*, Oedipus, at the beginning of the play, enjoys prosperity and reputation. Previously he has killed a stranger in a scuffle, and married a bride without due diligence. The discovery that the man he killed was his father and the woman he married was his mother leads to the overturning of his fortune, as he is banished from his kingdom and blinds himself in shame and remorse. See Introduction, p. xxii.

Danaus: in Greek mythology Danaus was the king of Argos, and was forced to consent to the marriage of his fifty daughters to their fifty Egyptian cousins. He gave each daughter a dagger with which to kill her husband on their wedding night. All did so except one, who spared her husband Lynceus; an act of disobedience for which she was put on trial by her father. The lost tragedy referred to by Aristotle clearly told a somewhat different story.

recognize Orestes: in Euripides' tragedy *Iphigeneia in Tauris*, whose plot Aristotle summarizes later at 1455b3.

32 *errs in some way*: the Greek word *hamartia* can cover both cognitive and moral error.

Thyestes: the uncle of Agamemnon, who was tricked into eating the flesh of his sons, and married a woman who was, unknown to him, his own daughter.

Alcmaeon . . . Telephus: Alcmaeon killed his mother Eriphyle in obedience to a command of his deceased father, who had been tricked by her into taking part in a fatal expedition. Meleager, a hunter in love with Atalanta, killed his brothers in a quarrel over her, whereupon his mother Althaia caused his death. Telephus, son of Heracles and king of Mysia, was wounded by Achilles while the Greek warriors were on their way to Troy; Euripides wrote a play about the subsequent history of his wound. The other characters in this list have been identified in previous notes.

33 *Orestes and Aegisthus*: Orestes was the son of Agamemnon and Clytemnestra. During the siege of Troy Aegisthus seduced Clytemnestra and joined with her in murdering Agamemnon on his return from the war. Orestes, with the help of his sister Electra, murdered Aegisthus and Clytemnestra in revenge.

34 *Medea kill her children*: in Euripides' tragedy, Medea, enraged by the desertion of her husband Jason, kills their children in revenge.

34 *Haemon and Creon in Antigone*: there is in fact plenty of suffering in Sophocles' tragedy of that name. Antigone, daughter of Oedipus, is betrothed to Haemon, the son of Creon, king of Thebes. For an act of disobedience she is buried alive in a cave. Haemon goes to the cave and discovers that she has hanged herself; when he is found by Creon he attempts to stab him, but misses and kills himself.

recognizes him in time: in a lost play by Euripides, Merope, the wife of Cresphontes, recognized her son when on the point of killing him in his sleep.

hand her over to the enemy: nothing is known of this play, and the episode here described does not figure in the surviving mythology of Helle, who fell off the ram with the golden fleece and was drowned in the sea now named after her, the Hellespont. Aristotle, in this passage, seems to be having second thoughts about his earlier condemnation of happy endings.

35 *moral character*: translates the Greek word *ethos* from which our 'ethics' is derived. Here the word refers principally to the moral status of individual characters in a tragedy, but also to the 'moral' of the story—its ethical message.

should be good: that is, better than us (48a1) but not perfect (53a8). The context shows that Aristotle has in mind the moral, not the social, status of the characters.

fundamental choice: the Greek word *prohairesis* represents a key concept in Aristotle's ethical system, that of the choice of a way of life.

Menelaus in Orestes: in Euripides' tragedy of this name, the protagonist is being tried by the citizens of Argos for the murder of his mother and her lover. His uncle Menelaus, dropping in on the way home from Troy to Sparta, is too cowardly to try to save him from the death penalty.

Melanippe: the heroine of Euripides' lost play *Melanippe the Wise*, apparently too clever by half.

not at all like her later self: the later self is the heroine of *Iphigeneia in Tauris* (frequently quoted in the *Poetics*). Another Euripidean tragedy, *Iphigeneia in Aulis*, shows her being sacrificed by her father Agamemnon on his way to Troy.

explication: the Greek word *lysis* is often rendered 'denouement', but that is too exotic and technical a rendering.

in the Medea: in Euripides' play of that name, Medea escapes in the Sun's chariot. In Greek staging, divinities appeared literally in a machine, an apparatus above the characters on stage.

in the Iliad: in Book Two of the *Iliad* the Greeks are about to abandon the siege of Troy and to sail away, but they are prevented by the goddess Athena.

36 *paradigm of stubbornness*: the Greek text is uncertain here; I accept an emendation of Lobel.

Tyro: Tyro bore two sons to the sea-god Poseidon and abandoned them in a boat—she identified them in later life by recognizing the boat.

bath scene: Odysseus, returning to Ithaca in disguise, is recognized by his scar while being bathed by his nurse Euryclea (*Odyssey* 19.386 ff.). Later he shows the same scar to some swineherds as a proof of his identity. Aristotle's other references in this paragraph are obscure.

37 *in Sophocles' Tereus*: Tereus, the king of Thrace, lusted after Philomela, raped her, and then cut out her tongue so that she could not reveal what had happened; however, she depicted the crime in a tapestry that she sent to her sister.

Orestes has come: in Aeschylus' *Choephorae* ('Libation-Bearers') Orestes returns from exile to avenge his father's death, and dedicates a lock of hair on his tomb. His sister Electra recognizes the hair (and a nearby footprint) as strikingly similar to her own.

on the latter: the disappearance of the three plays just mentioned by Aristotle makes it impossible to identify the events he is referring to.

39 *until the end*: the Greek text of this and the next paragraph is uncertain, and so are the plots of the lost plays.

plays set in the underworld: all the titles in this list figure among the works of Aeschylus, Sophocles, and Euripides, but all are lost except for Aeschylus' *Prometheus*, which is about the torments inflicted by Zeus on the Titan in punishment for giving humans fire and the arts.

40 *Sisyphus*: according to Greek mythology Sisyphus was the most cunning of men. He tricked the gods of the underworld into letting him return to earth after death. In punishment, on his return, he was made to roll uphill a stone which perpetually rolled back downhill just before reaching the summit.

41 *Protagoras*: a fifth-century sophist who was one of the first Greek grammarians.

42 *not a syllable*: the manuscript readings are faulty here: a 'not' has to be interpolated.

men . . . and de: these Greek particles express nuances that are often expressed in English merely by tone of voice. Aristotle's definition seems quite inappropriate, and is bafflingly repeated a few lines later: the text must undoubtedly be corrupt.

amphi, peri, and so on: here Aristotle gives two prepositions to illustrate the definition of a conjunction—further evidence that the text is corrupt.

42 *noun*: the Greek word *onoma* covers all nouns and adjectives as well as proper names.

provide examples: in English as in Greek the plural form of a noun is an inflection of the singular form. In the other cases the Greek language achieves by inflections the results that in English are more commonly managed by attaching a preposition to a noun or an auxiliary to a verb.

43 *Hermocaicoxanthus*: this word, otherwise unknown, appears to be a fusion of the names of three rivers.

a case of analogy: as the examples show, Aristotle uses 'metaphor' broadly to cover many different kinds of transference of meaning.

44 *one kind of stopping*: the generic term 'Stop' is transferred (i.e. used to refer to) a particular mode of stopping, namely being moored.

bowl of Ares: at this point one would expect a definition of euphemism which occurred in the earlier list between metaphor and coinage. Editors conjecture a lacuna in the manuscripts.

45 *word for vision*: the famous line is a fragment of Empedocles.

five in upsilon: Aristotle's list is very incomplete, and editors conjecture a lacuna.

bronze upon his fellow: the allusion is to the medical use of a cupping-glass.

46 *mixing his Hellebore*: it is impossible to render in English these (parodied) Homeric effects of lengthening a vowel. Perhaps an example from Shakespeare will help. 'Now is it Rome indeed and room enough.'

noisy shore: again, Aristotle's point can only be made in English by using examples from English dramatists. Compare 'the multitudinous seas incarnadine' with 'redden the many seas'.

elevate the style: English, as a non-inflected language, is less hospitable to changes of word order than Greek. However, several English poets have used this device to good effect. Cf. the last two lines of Arthur Hugh Clough's *Actaeon* about Diana: 'She, the liquid stream in, her limbs carelessly reclining, | The flowing waters collected grateful about her.'

47 *any single outcome*: in September 480 the Greek navies defeated the Persian forces at Salamis, and on the same day Greek colonists from Syracuse and Acragas routed the Carthaginians at Himera in Sicily.

48 *The Trial at Arms . . . Women of Troy*: some of these titles are creations of Aristotle's imagination. Others were actually dramatized by tragedians, such as Euripides' *Women of Troy* and Sophocles' *Philoctetes*.

49 *the latter for dancing, and the former for action*: on these, see the Note on Metre, p. 89.

50 *in the first place*: my translation renders one possible reconstruction of a corrupt Greek text.

problems and solutions: this difficult chapter is probably an abbreviation of the lost six books of Aristotle's *Homeric Problems*.

51 *is intrinsic*: this sentence translates a reconstruction of a defective Greek text.

52 *is ambiguous*: this paragraph sets out to remove apparent contradictions in passages of the *Iliad*. The detailed examples given do not admit of illuminating translation into other languages.

53 *went to Sparta*: in the fourth book of the *Odyssey* Odysseus' son Telemachus pays a visit to Sparta. Critics found it odd that there was no mention in the book of Icarius, his maternal grandfather.

is not possible: this translates a reconstruction of a defective Greek text.

Aegeus in Euripides: Aegeus, king of Athens, offers asylum to Medea in Euripides' play of that name.

54 *Mynniscus . . . Pindarus too*: Mynniscus acted in Aeschylus' tragedies; nothing is known of the other two actors.

SIDNEY, *AN APOLOGY FOR POETRY*

59 *Musaeus*: a mythical Greek poet, pupil of Orpheus.

Linus: the subject of various myths, according to one of which he was killed by Heracles with his own lyre.

Livius Andronicus: a third-century BC writer who translated the *Odyssey* into Latin verse.

60 *Solon . . . Plato*: Solon was a leading Athenian statesman of the sixth century BC. In addition to reforming the city's constitution he put many of his moral and political ideas into verse. The legend of Atlantis is mentioned in Plato's *Timaeus*.

Gyges' Ring: Plato, in the second book of his *Republic*, makes use of the legend of Gyges, who by means of a magic ring that made him invisible became king of Lydia.

63 *peizing*: 'weighing'.

66 *formidine poenae than virtutis amore*: 'more by fear of punishment than by love of virtue'.

69 *hoc opus, hic labor est*: 'this is the task, here is the effort' (Virgil, *Aeneid* 6.129).

70 *indulgere genio*: to follow one's fancy.

Menenius Agrippa: the story, recorded in Livy, is adapted in Shakespeare, *Coriolanus*, I. i.

71 *Nathan the Prophet*: in 2 Samuel 12: 1–7.

 Psalm of Mercy: Psalm 51.

SHELLEY, *A DEFENCE OF POETRY*

76 *Addison's Cato*: Addison's tragedy, produced in 1713, dealt with the suicide of the Roman republican in protest at the dictatorship of Julius Caesar.

SAYERS, 'ARISTOTLE ON DETECTIVE FICTION'

81 *Trent's Last Case . . . The Hound of the Baskervilles*: the former is a classic detective story by E. C. Bentley, published in 1913, the latter a 1902 novel by Arthur Conan Doyle, featuring Sherlock Holmes.

84 *Ulysses*: James Joyce's novel, first published in 1922.

86 *Father Knox*: Ronald A. Knox (1888–1957), Oxford wit, Roman Catholic convert, and Bible translator, was also a writer of detective stories such as *The Three Taps*.

GLOSSARY OF KEY TERMS

Action, conduct	*praxis*	
Art	*technē*	includes crafts and skills
Capacity	*dunamis*	also 'faculty', 'capability'
Character	*hexis*	see also 'moral character'
Choice	*prohairesis*	
Complication	*desis*	
Depraved	*mochtheros*	
Discovery	*anagnorēsis*	alternative translation: 'recognition'
Emotion	*pathos*	
Error	*amartia*	see note on p. 93
Explication	*lusis*	
Happiness	*eudaimonia*	
Ideas	*dianoia*	see Introduction, p. xxi
Knowledge	*epistēmē*	
Making	*poiesis*	see Introduction, p. xi
Moral character	*ēthos*	
Noble	*kalon*	also 'beautiful'
Pain	*lupe*	includes all kinds of distress, e.g. thirst
Passion	*pathos*	
Pleasure	*hēdonē*	
Plot	*systema tōn pragmatōn*	
Purification	*katharsis*	see Introduction, p. xxv
Reason	*logos*	also 'word'
Representation	*mimēsis*	alternative translation 'imitation': see p. xv
Reversal	*peripetia*	alternative translation 'overturning'
Story	*muthos*	alternative translation 'plot'; but see p. xix
Suffering	*pathos*	
Task	*ergon*	also 'work'
Virtue	*arēte*	also 'excellence'
Wicked	*ponēros*	

INDEX

American Literature

British and Irish Literature

Children's Literature

Classics and Ancient Literature

Colonial Literature

Eastern Literature

European Literature

Gothic Literature

History

Medieval Literature

Oxford English Drama

Poetry

Philosophy

Politics

Religion

The Oxford Shakespeare

A complete list of Oxford World's Classics, including Authors in Context, Oxford English Drama, and the Oxford Shakespeare, is available in the UK from the Marketing Services Department, Oxford University Press, Great Clarendon Street, Oxford OX2 6DP, or visit the website at www.oup.com/uk/worldsclassics.

In the USA, visit www.oup.com/us/owc for a complete title list.

Oxford World's Classics are available from all good bookshops. In case of difficulty, customers in the UK should contact Oxford University Press Bookshop, 116 High Street, Oxford OX1 4BR.

ALEXANDER POPE	Selected Poetry
ANN RADCLIFFE	The Italian The Mysteries of Udolpho The Romance of the Forest A Sicilian Romance
CLARA REEVE	The Old English Baron
SAMUEL RICHARDSON	Pamela
RICHARD BRINSLEY SHERIDAN	The School for Scandal and Other Plays
TOBIAS SMOLLETT	The Adventures of Roderick Random The Expedition of Humphry Clinker
LAURENCE STERNE	The Life and Opinions of Tristram Shandy, Gentleman A Sentimental Journey
JONATHAN SWIFT	Gulliver's Travels Major Works A Tale of a Tub and Other Works
JOHN VANBRUGH	The Relapse and Other Plays
HORACE WALPOLE	The Castle of Otranto
MARY WOLLSTONECRAFT	Mary and The Wrongs of Woman A Vindication of the Rights of Woman